Sally, Judith & David.

Christmas 1947.

ÆSOP'S FABLES

AGENTS

The United States
THE MACMILLAN COMPANY, NEW YORK
Australia and New Zealand
THE OXFORD UNIVERSITY PRESS, MELBOURNE
Canada
THE MACMILLAN COMPANY OF CANADA, TORONTO
South Africa
THE OXFORD UNIVERSITY PRESS, CAPE TOWN
India, Burma, China and F.M.S.
MACMILLAN AND COMPANY LIMITED
BOMBAY   CALCUTTA   MADRAS

The Fox and the Grapes

"'Let who will take them,' says he, 'they are but green and sour, so I'll even let them alone.'"

ÆSOP'S
FABLES

WITH EIGHT PAGE ILLUSTRATIONS

IN COLOUR BY

CHARLES FOLKARD

A. & C. BLACK, LTD.

4, 5 & 6 SOHO SQUARE, LONDON, W.1

Made in Great Britain

First published in October 1912
Reprinted in 1916 and 1918
Reissued in Black's Boys' and Girls' Library in 1927
Reprinted in 1939, 1941 and 1947

PRINTED BY
MORRISON AND GIBB LTD., LONDON AND EDINBURGH

I_F the great waters of the river of literature are traced back to their sources, they will be found in the folk-tales of the primitive peoples. Nearly every nation has evolved out of its folklore some form of beast-tale, and in certain instances these stories have been developed into a means of distilling the simple morals of a people still in the nursery of civilization. This process went on in India and in Greece, and through many devious channels there gradually grew together a collection of fables or beast-tales, which have for two thousand years and more been associated with the name of Æsop.

The few facts that are fairly well established concerning Æsop make a very inadequate biography. Writers in the seventeenth and following century, lacking the more exact and critical methods of to-day, accepted as more or less true the accretion of legend, which had formed during the long period since the fables came into being. Thus Sir Roger L'Estrange, relying on Planudes, describes the fabulist as "in his person deformed to the highest degree, flat-nos'd, hunchback'd, blobber-lipp'd, a long misshapen head, his body crooked all over, big-belly'd, baker-legg'd, and his complexion so swarthy that he took his very name from't, for Æsop is the same with Æthiop. . . ." A wonderfully elaborate description without any historical basis worth consideration! The main facts come from Herodotus. From him we learn that Æsop lived in the sixth century before Christ, was a slave of Iadmon, son of Hephæstopolis, a Samian, and was put to death by the men of Delphi in accordance with an oracle. Herodotus also says that "when the Delphians frequently made proclamation, in obedience to the oracle, for 'anyone who would require satisfaction for the death of Æsop,' no one else appeared, but another Iadmon, the grandson of this Iadmon, required it; thus Æsop must have belonged to Iadmon."*

Herodotus calls Æsop "the writer of fables,"

* "Euterpe," 134. Translated by Henry Cary, M.A., 1891.

PREFACE

and if he did actually commit his tales to writing,
it is quite probable that a great number of the
fables associated with his name did originate
with him, or, at least, become popular through
him. At the present time, however, there is only
complete evidence for attributing one solitary
fable to Æsop! This is the tale of the Fox and
the Hedgehog, given on p. 158 of this edition.
Aristotle* tells us that "Æsop, defending at
Samos a demagogue who was being tried for his
life, said that a Fox trying to cross a river was
once swept into a crevice in the rock, and, not
being able to get out, suffered miseries for a long
while, being covered with dog-fleas. A Hedgehog in his wanderings, seeing the Fox, took pity
on her, and asked whether he should remove the
fleas. The Fox objected, and, on the Hedgehog
asking him why, said: 'These are sated, and
draw little blood; but if you take them away
others will come with an appetite, and drain
what blood is left to me.' 'Now you, too,
Samians, will take no more hurt from this man,
for he is rich; but, if you kill him others will
come poor, and will fritter and waste your public
wealth.'"

* "Rhetoric," II. xx. 6. Translated by Sir R. C. Jebb
1909.

In another passage Aristotle* says "like Æsop's" or "the Libyan fables," which indicates a knowledge of a collection of fables associated with his name.

In Plutarch's "Septem Sapientum Convivium," Æsop is present on a mission from Crœsus to Periander, King of Corinth. It is also mentioned that he was on his way to consult the oracle at Delphi. At this banquet Æsop, sitting lower than Solon, gave the company this fable:

"A Lydian mule, viewing his own form in a river, admired the size and beauty of his body; and, raising his crest, he waxed proud, resolving to imitate the horse in his gait and fleetness, but presently recollecting his base extraction, that his father was but an ass at best, he stops his career and checks his haughtiness."

Demetrius Phalereus, who founded the great library of Alexandria *circa* 300 B.C., gathered up about two hundred fables, presumably all he could discover, and called them the "Assemblies of Æsopic Tales." This collection was edited and interpolated at Alexandria for three centuries, and then early in the Christian era a Greek named Phædrus, a freedman of Augustus, put

* "Rhetoric," II. xx. 3. Translated by Sir R. C. Jebb, 1909.

the whole collection "into neat Latin iambics."
Mr. Jacobs, whom I have quoted, who has put
together in scholarly fashion the results of the
learned researches of Tyrwhit, Crusius, Benfey,
Robert, Hervieux, and others, therefore writes:
" As the modern Æsop is mainly derived from
Phædrus, the answer to the question, 'Who wrote
Æsop?' is simply : 'Demetrius of Phaleron.'"*

Whether the Æsopic fables of ancient history
had really originated in India, the home of the
beast-fable with a moral application, or had
generated spontaneously in the Hellenic penin-
sula, is an absorbing subject on which a great
deal of learned inquiry has been concentrated by
French and German writers, to whom I must
refer the reader; but the books of fables of our own
times are not derived solely from Greek sources.
There came to Alexandria in the first century A.D.
a collection of about one hundred Indian fables,
and these appear to have had the distinctive
feature of a moral, or the lesson of the fable concentrated in a few brief words. Mr. Jacobs thinks
it probable that about three hundred years earlier
these stories, known as the " Fables of Kasyâpa,"
were taken to Ceylon, and it was by means of an
embassy from that island that they reached the

* " Æsop's Fables," p. xvi, 1894.

great centre of learning at the delta of the Nile.
There they were translated, becoming known as
the "Libyan Fables," and were attributed to
Kybises.

Thus, at the end of the first century A.D. there
were two groups of fables which a Roman, named
Nicostratus, brought together in the time of
Marcus Aurelius. The united Libyan and Deme-
trian groups numbered three hundred stories. In
the third century they were put into Greek verse
by Valerius Babrius. Until 1840 this Roman,
who was tutor to Branchus, a son of Alexander
Severus, was known through quotation and refer-
ence alone, but in that year a manuscript was
discovered in the convent of St. Laura on Mount
Athos by Minoides Menas, who had been en-
trusted with the task of searching in the
monasteries of Greece by the French Minister of
Public Instruction.

This manuscript is incomplete. It is arranged
alphabetically, and stops short at O, but the
identity of Babrius is no longer in doubt, and the
pedigree of the Æsopic fable was made more plain.

From these original sources endless transla-
tions and adaptations were made. Avian, one of
the earliest, made his towards the end of the
fourth century ; a small selection was turned into

x

prose in the ninth century, during the revival of learning under Charlemagne ; in the fourteenth century a Greek monk, named Maximus Planudes, probably produced the "Life of Æsop," and in 1484 Caxton produced at Westminster the first printed edition of the fables that appeared in England. He translated and edited the work himself, and reveals himself as something more than the mere printer of popular imagination. The heavy black-letter volume begins in this fashion :

" Here begynneth the book of the subtyl historyes and Fables of Esope whiche were translated out of Frensche into Englysche by Wylliam Caxton at Westmynstere. In the yere of oure Lorde MCCCCLXXXIII."

Since Caxton the popularity of the fables has been revealed in the endless new editions which have appeared in the succeeding centuries. In the great catalogue in the library of the British Museum there are thirty-six pages of entries. To those who are not concerned with the fascinating study of folklore and have passed out of the years of childhood, the fables associated with the name of Æsop make little appeal. They are not, as in the days of Solon, even mirth-producing to the adult mind. Like the raised beach of geology, the fable has ceased to be a part of adult literature, and is popular only with the juvenile portion of the community, who are in a few short years passing through the stages of mental evolution, which has taken Europe, as a whole, two thousand years to accomplish.

The fables contain much sound common sense, with here and there an excellent moral lesson, and they are so embedded in the foundations of our morality that such phrases as "the lion's share" or "blowing hot and cold" are seldom recognized as having an Æsopic origin.

GORDON HOME.

CONTENTS

ARRANGED ALPHABETICALLY

ÆSOP'S FABLES

CONTENTS

ÆSOP'S FABLES

CONTENTS

LIST OF ILLUSTRATIONS
IN COLOUR

Also numerous line illustrations in the text

xix

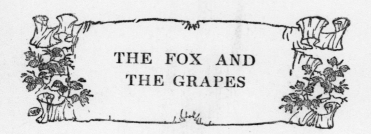

THE FOX AND THE GRAPES

A Fox, very hungry, chanced to come into a vineyard where there hung branches of charming ripe Grapes; but nailed up to a trellis so high that he leaped till he quite tired himself, without being able to reach one of them. At last says he:

"Let who will take them; they are but green and sour, so I'll even let them alone."

DO NOT PRETEND TO DESPISE WHAT YOU CANNOT OBTAIN.

FORTUNE AND THE BOY

A Boy was sleeping by the side of a well. Fortune saw him, and came and waked him, saying:

"Prithee, good Child, do not lie sleeping here, for if you should fall in nobody would impute it to you, but lay all the blame upon me, Fortune."

THE COVETOUS MAN

A POOR covetous wretch, who had scraped together a good parcel of money, went and dug a hole in one of his fields and hid it. The great pleasure of his life was to go and look upon this treasure once a day at least, which one of his servants observing, and guessing there was something more than ordinary in the place, came at night, found it, and carried it off. The next day, returning as usual to the scene of his delight, and perceiving it had been stolen from him, he tore his hair for grief, and uttered the doleful complaints of his despair to the woods and meadows. At last a neighbour of his, who knew his temper, overhearing him, and being informed of the cause of his sorrow

"Cheer up, man," says he; "thou hast lost nothing; there is the hole for thee to go and peep at still, and if thou canst but fancy thy money there, it will do just as well."

TREASURE UNUSED MIGHT JUST AS WELL NOT EXIST.

THE LION AND THE FROG

A LION, hearing an odd kind of a hollow voice, and seeing nobody, started up; he listened again, and perceiving the voice to continue, even trembled and quaked for fear. At last, seeing a Frog crawl out of the lake, and finding that the noise he had heard was nothing but the croaking of that little creature, he went up to it, and partly out of anger, partly contempt, spurned it to pieces with his feet.

A FOOLISH FEAR UNNERVES THE MIGHTIEST.

THE KITE & THE PIGEONS

A KITE, who had kept sailing in the air for many days near a dove-house, and made a dart at several Pigeons, but all to no purpose — for they were too nimble for him—at last had recourse to stratagem, and took his opportunity one day to make a declaration to them, in which he set forth his own just and good intentions, who had nothing more at heart than the defence and protection of the Pigeons in their ancient rights and liberties; and how concerned he was at their fears and jealousies of a foreign invasion, especially their unjust and unreasonable suspicions of himself, as if he intended by force of arms to break in upon their constitution and erect a tyrannical government over them. To prevent all which, and thoroughly to quiet their minds,

4

he thought proper to propose to them such terms
of alliance and articles of peace as might for ever
cement a good understanding betwixt them ; the
principal of which was that they should accept
of him for their king, and give him all kingly
privilege and power over them. The poor simple
Pigeons consented. The Kite took the corona-
tion oath after a very solemn manner, on his
part, and the Doves the oaths of allegiance and
fidelity, on theirs. But much time had not
passed over their heads before the good Kite
pretended that it was part of his prerogative to
devour a Pigeon whenever he pleased. And this
he was not contented to do himself only, but
instructed the rest of the royal family in the
same kingly arts of government. The Pigeons,
reduced to this miserable condition, said one to
the other :

"Ah, we deserve no better. Why did we let
him come ?"

THE MICE IN
COUNCIL

THE Mice called a general council; and having
met after the doors were locked, entered into a
free consultation about ways and means to
render their fortunes and estates more secure
from the danger of the Cat. Many things were
offered, and much was debated, *pro* and *con*,
upon the matter. At last a young Mouse, in a
fine flowery speech, suggested a plan, and that
the only one, which was to put them for the
future entirely out of the power of the enemy;
and this was, that the Cat should wear a bell
about her neck, which, upon the least motion,
would give the alarm, and be a signal for them
to retire into their holes. This speech was received with great applause, and it was even pro-

posed by some, that the Mouse who made it should have the thanks of the assembly. Upon which, an old grave Mouse, who had sat silent all the while, stood up, and in another speech, owned that the contrivance was admirable, and the author of it, without doubt a clever Mouse.

"But," he said, "he thought it would not be so proper to vote him thanks, till he should farther inform them how this bell was to be fastened about the Cat's neck, and what Mouse would undertake to do it."

IT IS EASY TO PROPOSE IMPOSSIBLE REMEDIES.

THE BLACKAMOOR

A CERTAIN man having bought a Blackamoor was so simple as to think that the colour of his skin was only dirt and filth, which he had contracted for want of due care under his former master. This fault he fancied might easily be removed. So he ordered the poor Black to be put into a tub, and was at a considerable charge in providing ashes, soap, and scrubbing brushes for the operation. To work they went, rubbing and scouring his skin all over, but to no manner of purpose, for when they had repeated their washings several times and were grown quite weary, all they got by it was that the wretched Blackamoor caught cold and died.

WE CANNOT AFFORD TO BE IGNORANT.

THE BLACKAMOOR

"To work they went, rubbing and scouring his skin all over, but to no manner of purpose."

THE FOX
AND THE STORK

A Fox invited a Stork to dinner, and, being inclined to amuse himself at the expense of his guest, provided nothing for the entertainment but soup in a wide shallow dish. This he could lap up with a great deal of ease, but the Stork, who could but just dip in the point of his bill, was not a bit the better all the while. However, in a few days he returned the compliment and invited the Fox, but suffered nothing to be brought to table but some minced meat in a glass jar, the neck of which was so deep and so narrow, that though the Stork, with his long bill, made a very good meal, all that the Fox, who was very hungry, could do, was to lick the food which the Stork dropped on the rim. Reynard was heartily vexed at first; but when he came to take his leave, he owned ingenuously that he had been used as he deserved, and that he had no reason to take any treatment ill, of which he had himself set the example.

MEAN FOLK ARE SOMETIMES PAID BACK WITH THEIR OWN COIN.

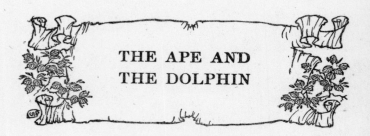

THE APE AND THE DOLPHIN

A SHIP, wrecked off the coast of Greece, had on board a large Ape, kept for the amusement of the sailors. The ship went down, and the Ape and most of the crew were left struggling in the water. Dolphins are said to have a great friendship for man, and one of those fishes, mistaking the Ape for a man, came under him and, supporting him on his back, swam with him to the mouth of the Piræus (the harbour of Athens).

THE APE AND THE DOLPHIN

"In what part of Greece do you live?" demanded the Dolphin.

"I am an Athenian,' said the Ape.

"Oh, then you know Piræus, of course?" said the Dolphin.

"Know Piræus!" cried the Ape, not wishing to appear ignorant to the Dolphin; "I should rather think I did. Why, my father and he are first cousins."

Thereupon the Dolphin, finding that he was supporting an impostor, slipped from beneath his legs, and left him to his fate.

THE LION & OTHER BEASTS

THE Lion and several other beasts entered into an alliance, offensive and defensive, and were to live very sociably together in the forest. One day, having made a sort of an excursion by way of hunting, they took a very fine, large, fat Deer, which was divided into four parts; there happening to be then present his Majesty the Lion, and only three others. After the division was made and the parts set out, his Majesty, advancing forward some steps and pointing to one of the shares, was pleased to declare himself after the following manner:

"This I seize and take possession of as my right, which devolves to me, as I am descended by a true, lineal, hereditary succession from the royal family of Lion; that (pointing to the second), I claim by I think no unreasonable demand, considering that all the engagements you have with the enemy turn chiefly upon my courage and conduct, and you very well know that wars are too expensive to be carried on without proper supplies. Then (nodding his head towards the third), that I shall take by virtue of my royal power; to which I make no question, but so dutiful and loyal a people will pay all the deference and regard that I can desire. Now, as for the remaining part, the necessity of our present affairs is so very urgent, our stock so low, and our credit so impaired and weakened, that I must insist upon your granting that without any hesitation or demur; and hereof fail not at your peril."

THERE IS NO CERTAIN REWARD FOR THOSE WHO SHARE
THE TOIL WITH THE MIGHTY.

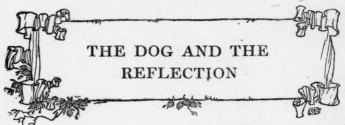

THE DOG AND THE REFLECTION

A DOG, crossing a little rivulet with a piece of flesh in his mouth, saw his own reflection represented in the clear mirror of the limpid stream, and believing it to be another Dog who was carrying another piece of flesh, he could not forbear catching at it; but was so far from getting anything by his greedy design, that he dropped the piece he had in his mouth, which immediately sank to the bottom, and was lost.

IN GRASPING AT THE SHADOW YOU MAY LOSE THE SUBSTANCE.

THE COCK AND THE JEWEL

A BRISK young Cock, in company with two or three pullets, was raking up straw in a farmyard in a search for food, and happened to scratch up a jewel. He knew what it was well enough, for it sparkled with an exceeding bright lustre; but, not knowing what to do with it, endeavoured to cover his ignorance under a gay contempt. So, shrugging up his wings and shaking his head, he expressed himself to this purpose:

"Indeed you are a very fine thing, but I know not any business you have here. I make no scruple of declaring that my taste lies quite another way, and I had rather have one grain of dear, delicious barley than all the jewels under the sun."

PRECIOUS THINGS ARE ONLY VALUABLE TO THOSE WHO
KNOW THEIR WORTH.

THE STAG LOOKING INTO THE WATER

A STAG that had been drinking at a clear spring saw himself in the water, and, pleased with the prospect, stood afterwards for some time contemplating and surveying his shape and features, from head to foot.

"Ah," says he, "what a glorious pair of branching horns are there! How gracefully do those antlers hang over my forehead and give an agreeable turn to my whole face! If some other parts of my body were but proportionate to them I would turn my back to nobody, but I have a set of such legs as really makes me ashamed to see them. People may talk what they please of their conveniences, and what great need we stand in of them upon several occasions; but, for my part, I find them so very slender and unsightly that I had as lief have none at all."

16

A STAG LOOKING INTO THE WATER

While he was giving himself these airs he was alarmed with the noise of some huntsmen and a pack of hounds, that had been just laid on upon the scent, and were making towards him. Away he raced in some consternation, and, bounding nimbly over the plain, threw dogs and men at a vast distance behind him, after which, taking a very thick copse, he had the ill-fortune to be entangled by his horns in a thicket, where he was held fast till the hounds came in and pulled him down. Finding now how it was like to go with him in the pangs of death, he is said to have uttered these words:

"Unhappy creature that I am! I am too late convinced that what I prided myself in has been the cause of my undoing, and what I so much disliked was the only thing that could have saved me."

IN THE HOUR OF DANGER WHAT WE PRIZE MOST IS OFTEN OF LEAST SERVICE.

THE TRAVELLERS AND THE BEAR

Two Men, having to travel through a forest together, mutually promised to stand by each other in any danger they should meet upon the way. They had not gone far before a Bear came rushing towards them out of a thicket; upon which one, being a light nimble fellow, got up into a tree, the other, falling flat upon his face and holding his breath, lay still, while the Bear came up and smelled at him, but that creature, supposing him to be a dead carcass, went back again into the wood, without doing him the least harm. When all was over, the spark who had climbed the tree came down to his companion, and with a pleasant smile asked him what the Bear said to him; "for," said he, " I took notice that he clapped his mouth very close to your ear."

"Why," replies the other, " he charged me to take care for the future, not to put any confidence in such cowardly rascals as you are."

HE IS NO FRIEND WHO DESERTS YOU IN THE MOMENT
OF DANGER.

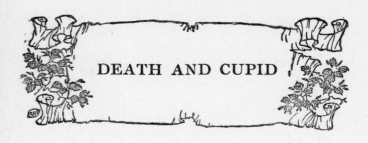

DEATH AND CUPID

CUPID one sultry summer's noon, tired with play and faint with heat, to rest himself went into a cool grotto, which happened to be the cave of Death. He threw himself carelessly down on the floor, and his quiver turning topsy-turvy, all the arrows fell out and mingled with those of Death, which lay scattered up and down the place. When he awoke he gathered them up as well as he could, but they were so intermingled, that though he knew the certain number he could not rightly distinguish them; from which it happened, that he took up some of the arrows which belonged to Death, and left several of his own in place of them. This is the cause that we, now and then, see the hearts of the old and decrepit transfixed with the bolts of Love; and with equal grief and surprise, behold those who are young and beautiful smitten with the darts of Death.

THE FOX AND THE ASS

AN Ass finding a Lion's skin, disguised himself with it and ranged about the forest, putting all the beasts that saw him into the greatest fear. After he had amused himself thus for some time, he met a Fox; and being desirous to frighten him, too, as well as the rest, he leapt at him with some fierceness and endeavoured to imitate the roaring of the Lion.

"Your humble servant," says the Fox, "if you had held your tongue I might have taken you for a Lion, as others did; but now you bray, I know who you are."

YOU CAN KNOW A FOOL BY HIS WORDS.

THE RAVEN AND THE SERPENT

A HUNGRY Raven, flying about in quest of his prey, saw a Serpent basking himself upon the side of a sunny bank ; down he pounced upon him, and seized him with his horny beak in order to devour him, but the Serpent, writhing to and fro with the pain, bit the Raven again and again with his venomous teeth to such a degree that he could not survive it. The Raven, in the agonies of death, is said to have confessed that this judgment happened to him justly, since he had attempted to satisfy his craving appetite at the expense of another's welfare.

THE GARDENER AND HIS DOG

A GARDENER's Dog, frisking about the brink of a well in the garden, happened to fall into it. The Gardener very readily ran to his assistance, but as he was endeavouring to help him out, the cur bit him by the hand. The man took this un-gratefulness so unkindly, that he left him to shift for himself with this expostulation :

"Wicked wretch," quoth he, "are you so unreasonable as to injure the hand that comes to save your life, the hand of me, your master, who have hitherto fed and taken care of you! Die, as you deserve, for so mischievous and ill-natured a creature is not fit to live."

A DOG WILL SOMETIMES BITE THE HAND THAT SAVES IT.

THE BULL AND THE GOAT

A BULL, being pursued by a Lion, made towards the cave in which he designed to secure himself, but was opposed just at the entrance by a Goat, who had got possession before him, threatening a kind of defiance with his horns, seemingly resolved to dispute the pass with him. The Bull, who thought he had no time to lose in a contest of this nature, immediately made off again, but told the Goat that it was not for fear of him or his defiances.

"For," says he, "if the Lion were not so near, I would soon make you know the difference between a Bull and a Goat."

DO NOT TAKE ADVANTAGE OF ANOTHER'S MISFORTUNES.

THE EAGLE AND
THE FOX

AN Eagle that had young ones, looking out for something with which to feed them, happened to spy a Fox's cub, that lay basking itself abroad in the sun. She made a swoop and seized it immediately, but before she had carried it quite off the old Fox, coming home, implored her with tears in her eyes, to spare her cub and pity the distress of a poor fond mother, who should think no affliction so great as that of losing her child. The Eagle, whose nest was up in a very high tree, thought herself secure enough from all projects of revenge, and so bore away the cub to her young ones without showing any regard to the supplication of the Fox. But that subtle creature, highly incensed at this outrageous barbarity, ran to an altar, where some country people had been sacrificing a kid in the open fields, and catching up a firebrand in her mouth, made towards the tree where the Eagle's nest was, with a resolution of revenge. She had scarcely ascended the first branches when the Eagle, terrified with the approaching ruin of herself and family, begged of the Fox to desist, and with much submission returned her the cub again, safe and sound.

DO NOT UNDERESTIMATE THE POWER OF THOSE BENEATH YOU.

THE WOLF AND THE KID

A GOAT, going abroad to feed, shut up her young Kid at home, charging him to bolt the door fast, and open it to nobody till she herself should return. A Wolf, who lay lurking just by, heard this charge given, and soon afterwards came and knocked at the door, imitating the voice of the Goat, and desiring to be admitted. The Kid, looking out at a window and finding the cheat, bid him go about his business, for, however he might imitate a Goat's voice, yet he appeared too much like a Wolf to be trusted.

BE WARNED BY APPEARANCES.

THE ASS AND THE
LION HUNTING

A Lion took a fancy to hunt in company with an Ass, and, to make him the more useful, gave him instructions to hide himself in a thicket, and then to bray in the most frightful manner that he could possibly contrive.

"By this means," says he, "you will rouse all the beasts within hearing of you; while I stand at the outlets, and take them as they are making off."

This was done, and the stratagem took effect accordingly. The Ass brayed most hideously, and the timorous beasts, not knowing what to make of it, began to hurry away as fast as they could, when the Lion, who was posted at a proper avenue, seized and devoured them as he pleased. Having eaten until he was full he called out to the Ass, and bid him leave off, telling him he had done enough. Upon this the lop-eared brute came out of his ambush, and, approaching the Lion, asked him with an air of conceit how he liked his performance.

"Prodigiously," says he. "You did it so well that I protest, had I not known your nature and temper, I might have been frightened myself."

A COWARD IS NOT FEARED BY THOSE WHO KNOW HIM.

THE VAIN JACKDAW

A CERTAIN Jackdaw was so proud and ambitious, that, not contented to live within his own sphere, he picked up the feathers which fell from the Peacocks, stuck them among his own, and very confidently introduced himself into an assembly of those beautiful birds. They soon found him out, stripped him of his borrowed plumes, and, falling upon him with their sharp bills, punished him as his presumption deserved. Upon this, full

THE VAIN JACKDAW

of grief and affliction, he returned to his old companions, and would have flocked with them again ; but they, knowing his late life and conversation, industriously avoided him and refused to admit him into their company, and one of them at the same time gave him this serious reproof.

"If, friend, you could have been contented with your station and had not disdained the rank in which nature had placed you, you had not been used so scurvily by those upon whom you introduced yourself, nor suffered the slight which we now think ourselves obliged to put upon you."

FINE FEATHERS DO NOT MAKE FINE BIRDS.

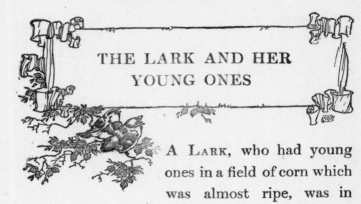

THE LARK AND HER YOUNG ONES

A LARK, who had young ones in a field of corn which was almost ripe, was in some fear lest the reapers should come to reap it before her young brood was fledged, and able to remove from the place. Wherefore, upon flying abroad to look for food, she left this charge with them: That they should take notice what they heard talked of in her absence, and tell her of it when she came back again. When she was gone, they heard the owner of the corn call to his son;

"Well," says he, "I think this corn is ripe enough; I would have you go early to-morrow, and desire our friends and neighbours to come and help us to reap it."

When the old Lark came home, the young ones fell a quivering and chirping round her, and told her what had happened, begging her to remove them as fast as she could. The mother bid them be easy, "for," says she, "if the owner depends upon his friends and neighbours, I am pretty sure the corn will not be reaped to-morrow."

Next day she went out again upon the same occasion, and left the same orders with them as before.

The owner came, and stayed, expecting those he had sent to; but the sun grew hot, and nothing was done, for not a soul came to help him.

"Then," says he to his son, "I perceive these friends of ours are not to be depended upon, so that you must even go to your uncles and cousins, and tell them I desire they would be here betimes to-morrow morning to help us to reap."

Well, this the young ones, in a great fright, reported also to their mother.

"If that be all," says she, "do not be frightened, children, for kindred and relations are not so very forward to serve one another; but take particular notice what you hear said the next time, and be sure you let me know it."

She went abroad the next day as usual; and the owner, finding his relations as slack as the rest of his neighbours, said to his son :

"Harkee, George, do you get a couple of good sickles ready against to-morrow morning, and we will even reap the corn ourselves."

When the young ones told their mother this, "Then," says she, "we must be gone indeed; for when a man undertakes to do his business himself, it is not so likely he will be disappointed."

So she removed her young ones immediately, and the corn was reaped the next day by the good man and his son.

IF YOU WANT A THING DONE, DO IT YOURSELF.

THE GOAT-HERD AND THE SHE-GOAT

A BOY, whose business it was to tend some Goats, as night came on collected them together and began to take them home. But one of the herd, a She-Goat, refused to take any notice of the boy's call, and continued to nibble the grass

THE GOAT-HERD AND SHE-GOAT

that grew on the ledge of rock where she stood.
At last the young Goat-Herd lost his patience,
and, picking up a stone, flung it at the dis-
obedient Goat. It struck one of her horns,
which broke off in the middle. Being frightened
at what he had done, and fearing his master's
anger, the boy fell on his knees in front of the
Goat and implored her not to say a word about
the damage he had done, for he had no idea of
aiming so well.

"Tush!" said the Goat, "if my tongue were
altogether silent, my horn will be bound to tell
the tale."

THE TRUTH WILL OUT.

THE STAG AND
THE FAWN

A STAG, grown old and mischievous, was, according to custom, stamping with his foot, making offers with his head, and bellowing so terribly that the whole herd quaked for fear of him; when one of the little Fawns, coming up, addressed him to this purpose:

"Pray, what is the reason that you, who are so stout and formidable at all other times, if you do but hear the cry of the hounds, are ready to fly out of your skin for fear?"

"What you observe is true," replied the Stag, "though I know not how to account for it. I am indeed vigorous and able enough, I think, to make my party good anywhere, and often resolve with myself that nothing shall ever dismay my courage for the future; but, alas! I no sooner hear the voice of a hound but all my spirits fail me, and I cannot help making off as fast as my legs can carry me."

THE EAGLE, THE CAT, AND THE SOW

"The Cat . . . putting on a sorrowful face: 'I hope,' says she, 'you do not
intend to go abroad to-day?'"

THE EAGLE, THE CAT, AND THE SOW

AN Eagle had built her nest upon the top branches of an old Oak. A wild Cat inhabited a hole in the middle, and in the hollow part at the bottom was a Sow, with a whole litter of Pigs. A happy neighbourhood, and might long have continued so had it not been for the wicked insinuations of the designing Cat. For, first of all, up she crept to the Eagle:

"Good neighbour," says she, "we shall be all undone; that wretched Sow yonder does nothing but lie at the foot of the tree, and, as I suspect, intends to grub it up, that she may the more easily come at our young ones. For my part, I will take care of my own concerns; you may do as you please, but I will watch her motions, though I stay at home this month for it."

When she had said this, which could not fail

of putting the Eagle into a great fright, down she went, and made a visit to the Sow at the bottom, and, putting on a sorrowful face:

"I hope," says she, "you do not intend to go abroad to-day?"

"Why not?" says the Sow.

"Nay," replies the other, "you may do as you please; but I overheard the Eagle tell her young ones that she would treat them with a Pig the first time she saw you go out, and I am not sure but she may take up with a Kitten in the meantime, so good-morrow to you. You will excuse me; I must go and take care of the little folks at home."

Away she went accordingly; and by contriving to steal out softly a-nights for her prey, and to stand watching and peeping all day at her hole, as under great concern, she made such an impression upon the Eagle and the Sow that neither of them dared venture abroad for fear of the other. The consequence of which was that themselves and their young ones in a little time were all starved, and made prizes of, by the treacherous Cat and her Kittens.

BEWARE OF TALE-TELLERS.

THE FOX AND THE BRAMBLE

A Fox, hard pressed by the Hounds, was getting over a hedge, but tore his foot upon a Bramble which grew just in the midst of it, upon which he reproached the Bramble for his inhospitable cruelty, in using a stranger which had fled to him for protection after such a barbarous manner

"Yes," says the Bramble, "you intended to have made me serve your turn, I know ; but take this piece of advice with you for the future, never lay hold of a Bramble again as you tender your sweet person, for laying hold is a privilege that belongs to us Brambles, and we do not care to let it go out of the family."

YOU CANNOT BE FAMILIAR WITH EVERYONE.

THE OLD MAN AND DEATH

A poor feeble old Man, who had crawled out into a neighbouring wood to gather a few sticks, had made up his bundle, and, laying it over his shoulders, was trudging homeward with it; but what with age, and the length of the way, and the weight of his burden, he grew so faint and weak that he sunk under it, and, as he sat on the ground, called upon Death to come, once for all, and ease him of his troubles. Death no sooner heard him but he came and demanded of him what he wanted. The poor old creature, who little thought Death had been so near, and frightened almost out of his senses with his terrible aspect, answered him, trembling, that having by chance let his bundle of sticks fall, and being too infirm to get it up himself, he had made bold to call upon him to help him; that, indeed, this was all he wanted at present, and that he hoped his worship was not offended with him for the liberty he had taken in so doing.

IT WOULD NOT BE WELL FOR US IF WE RECEIVED ALL
WE WISHED FOR.

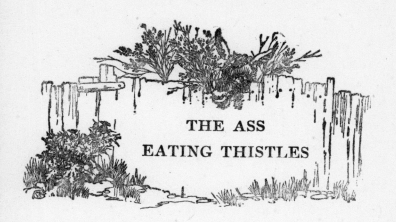

THE ASS
EATING THISTLES

AN Ass was loaded with good provisions of several sorts, which, in time of harvest, he was carrying into the field for his master and the reapers to dine upon. By the way he met with a fine large thistle, and, being very hungry, began to munch it, and while he did so he entered into this reflection : How many greedy lovers of good food would think themselves happy, amidst such a variety of delicate viands as I now carry ? But to me, this bitter, prickly thistle is more savoury and relishing than the most exquisite and sumptuous banquet.

ONE MAN'S MEAT IS ANOTHER MAN'S POISON.

THE OLD LION

A Lion, worn out with age, lay fetching his last gasp, and agonizing in the convulsive struggles of death. Upon which occasion several of the beasts, who had formerly been sufferers by him, came and revenged themselves upon him. The Boar with his mighty tusks, drove at him a stroke that glanced like lightning. And the Bull gored him with his violent horns. Which when the Ass saw they might do without any danger, he too came up, and threw his heels into the Lion's face. Upon which the poor old expiring tyrant uttered these words with his last dying groan:

"Alas! how grievous is it to suffer insults, even from the brave and the valiant; but to be spurned by so base a creature as this is, who is the disgrace of nature, is worse than dying ten thousand deaths !"

WE REAP WHAT WE SOW

THE WOLVES AND THE SHEEP

THE Wolves and the Sheep had been a long time in a state of war together. At last a cessation of arms was proposed in order to make a treaty of peace, and hostages were to be delivered on both sides for security. The Wolves proposed that the Sheep should give up their Dogs on the one side, and that they would deliver up their young ones on the other. This proposal was agreed to, but no sooner executed than the young Wolves began to howl for want of their mothers. The old ones took this opportunity to cry out that the treaty was broken, and so falling upon the sheep who were destitute of their faithful guardians the Dogs, they worried and devoured them without resistance.

YOU CAN NEVER MAKE PEACE WITH EVIL.

THE OLD MAN, HIS SON, AND THE ASS

AN old man and his little boy were once driving an Ass before them to the next market-town, where it was to be sold.

"Have you no more wit," said a passer-by, "than for you and your Son to trudge on foot, and let your Ass go light?"

So the Man put his Boy on the Ass, and they went on again.

"You lazy young rascal!" said the next person they met; "are you not ashamed to ride, and let your poor old Father go on foot?"

The Man lifted off the Boy, and got up himself.

Two Women passed soon after, and one said to the other, "Look at that selfish old fellow, riding on, while his little Son follows after on foot!"

The old Man thereupon took up the Boy behind him.

The next traveller they met asked the old Man whether or not the Ass was his own.

THE HORSE AND THE LION

Being answered that it was: "No one would think so," said he, "from the way in which you use it. Why, you are better able to carry the poor animal than he is to carry both of you."

So the old Man tied the Ass's legs to a long pole, and he and his Son shouldered the pole, and staggered along under the weight. In that fashion they entered the town, and their appearance caused so much laughter, that the old Man, mad with vexation at the result of his endeavours to give satisfaction to everybody, threw the Ass into the river, and seizing his Son by the arm, went his way home again.

PLEASE ALL AND YOU WILL PLEASE NONE.

THE HORSE AND THE LION

A LION, seeing a fine plump Nag, had a great mind to eat a bit of him, but knew not which way to get him into his power. At last he bethought himself of this contrivance: he gave out that he was a physician, who, having gained experience by his travels into foreign countries,

41

had made himself capable of curing any sort of malady or distemper, likely to come upon any kind of beast; hoping by this stratagem to get an easier admittance among cattle, and find an opportunity to execute his design. The Horse, who became aware of his plan, was resolved to be even with him; and so humoring the thing, as if he suspected nothing, he prayed the Lion to give him his advice in relation to a thorn he had got in his foot, which had quite lamed him, and gave him great pain and uneasiness.

The Lion readily agreed, and desired to see the foot. Upon which the Horse lifted up one of his hind legs, and while the Lion pretended to be poring earnestly upon the hoof, gave him such a kick in the face as quite stunned him and left him sprawling upon the ground. In the meantime the Horse trotted away, neighing, and laughing merrily at the success of the trick by which he had defeated the purpose of one who intended to have tricked him out of his life.

WARINESS CAN OVERCOME TREACHERY.

THE THIEVES AND THE COCK

SOME Thieves, entering a house with a design to rob it when they were safely in, found nothing worth taking but a Cock, so they carried him off. But as they were about to kill him he begged hard for his life, putting them in mind how useful he was to mankind by crowing and calling them up by times to their work.

"You villain," replied they, "it is for that very reason we will wring your neck off, for you alarm and keep people waking, so that we cannot rob in quiet because of you."

YOU CANNOT BE ESTEEMED BY GOOD AND BAD ALIKE.

THE ENVIOUS MAN AND THE COVETOUS

AN envious Man happened to be offering up his prayers to Jupiter just in the time and place with a covetous, miserable fellow. Jupiter, not caring to be troubled with their impertinences himself, sent Apollo to examine the merits of their petitions, and to give them such relief as he should think proper. Apollo therefore opened his commission, and told them that to make short of the matter, whatever the one asked, the other should have it double. Upon this the covetous Man, though he had a thousand things to request, yet forbore to ask first, hoping to receive a double quantity, for he concluded that all men's wishes sympathized with his. By this means the envious Man had an opportunity of making his petition first, which was the thing he aimed at; so without much hesitation he prayed to have one of his eyes put out, knowing that of consequence his companion would be deprived of both.

VICES ARE THEIR OWN PUNISHMENT.

THE TRAVELLERS AND THE CROW

SOME Travellers who had just started on a journey had only gone a short distance when a one-eyed Crow flew right over their path. Because of this bad omen they were thinking of giving up the journey, at least, for that day, and returning home.

"How foolish," said one of the travellers, who was of a jolly and mocking disposition, "if this silly Crow could tell what is about to happen to us, he would be as clever on his own account, and therefore would not have allowed himself to get one of his eyes knocked out."

THE CAT AND THE MICE

A CERTAIN house was much infested with Mice, but at last they got a Cat, who caught and ate some of them every day. The Mice, finding their numbers grow thin, consulted what was best to be done for the preservation of the public from the jaws of the devouring Cat. They debated, and came to this resolution, that no one should go down below the upper shelf. The Cat, observing the Mice no longer came down as usual, hungry and disappointed of her prey, had recourse to this stratagem; she hung by her hind legs on a peg which stuck in the wall, and pretended to be dead, hoping by this means to entice the Mice to come down. She had not been in this posture long before a cunning old Mouse peeped over the edge of the shelf, and spoke thus:

"Aha, my good friend, are you there? There you may be! I would not trust myself with you though your skin were stuffed with straw."

ONCE BITTEN TWICE SHY.

THE FOX AND THE WOLF

A Wolf having laid in store of provisions, kept close at home, and made much of himself. A Fox observed this, and thinking it something particular, went to visit him, the better to inform himself of the truth of the matter. The Wolf excused himself from seeing him by pretending he was very much indisposed. All this did but confirm the Fox in his suspicions: so away he goes to a Shepherd, telling him that he had nothing else to do but come with a good weapon, and knock the Wolf on the head as he lay in his cave. The Shepherd followed his directions, and killed the Wolf. The wicked Fox enjoyed the cave and provisions to himself, but not for long, for the same Shepherd, passing afterwards by the same hole and seeing the Fox there, despatched him also.

DO NOT INFORM UPON YOUR NEIGHBOUR FOR YOUR OWN ADVANTAGE.

THE LION, THE ASS, AND THE FOX

A LION, an Ass, and a Fox, went a hunting together in the forest; and it was agreed, that whatever was taken should be divided amongst them. They happened to have very good sport, and caught a large fat Stag, which the Lion ordered the Ass to divide. The Ass, according to the best of his capacity, did so, and made three pretty equal shares. But such fair methods not suiting at all the craving temper of the greedy Lion, without farther delay he flew upon the Ass, and tore him in pieces; and then bid the Fox divide it into two parts.

Reynard, who seldom wanted a prompter, however, had his cue given him sufficiently upon this occasion; and so, nibbling off one little bit for himself, he laid forth all the rest for the Lion's portion. The royal brute was so delighted at this dutiful and handsome proof of his respect, that he could not help expressing the satisfaction it gave him; and asked him where he could possibly have learnt so proper and so courtly a behaviour?

THE GOAT AND THE LION

" Why," replies Reynard, " to tell your majesty the truth, I was taught it by the Ass that lies dead there."

WE CAN LEARN MUCH FROM THE EXPERIENCES OF OTHERS.

THE GOAT AND THE LION

A LION, seeing a Goat upon a steep, craggy rock where he could not come at him, asked him what delight he could take to skip from one precipice to another all day, and venture the breaking of his neck every moment.

" I wonder," says he, " you will not come down and feed on the plain here, where there is plenty of good grass and fine sweet herbs."

" Why," replies the Goat, " I cannot but say your opinion is right; but you look so very hungry and designing that, to tell you the truth, I do not care to venture my person where you are."

PLEASANT PLACES ARE NOT ALWAYS THE SAFEST.

THE SHEPHERD TURNED MERCHANT

A SHEPHERD that kept his sheep near the sea, one clear summer's day drove them close to the shore, and sat down upon a piece of a rock to enjoy the cool breeze that came from the water. The green sea appeared calm and smooth, and Thetis, with her train of smiling and beautiful nymphs, seemed to dance upon the floating surface of the deep. The Shepherd's heart thrilled with secret pleasure, and he began to wish for the life of a merchant.

"Oh, how happy," says he, "should I be to plough this liquid plain in a trim vessel of my own; and to visit the remote parts of the world, instead of sitting idly here, to look upon a parcel of senseless sheep while they are grazing. Then what ample returns should I make in the way of traffic, and what a short and certain path would this be to riches and honour."

In short, this thought was improved into a resolution. Away he posted with all expedition, sold his flock and all that he had, then he bought a barque and fitted it out for a voyage; he loaded it with a cargo of dates, and set sail for a market that was held upon the coast of Asia, five hundred leagues off. He had not long been at sea before the wind began to blow tempestuously, and the waves to rage and swell; the violence of the weather increased, his ship was in danger of sinking, and he was obliged to lighten her by throwing all his dates overboard. After this his vessel was driven upon a rock near the shore and battered to pieces, he himself hardly escaping with life. Poor, and destitute of subsistence, he applied himself to the man who had bought his flock, and was allowed to tend it as a hireling. He sat in the same place as before, and the ocean again looked calm and smooth.

" Ah," says he, " deceitful, tempting element, in vain you try to engage me a second time; my misfortunes have left me too poor to be again deluded in the same way, and experience has made me so wise as to resolve, whatever my condition may be, never to trust thy faithless bosom more."

EXPERIENCE IS A HARD SCHOOL.

THE APE AND HER TWO YOUNG ONES

An Ape having two young ones, was dotingly fond of one, but disregarded and slighted the other. One day she chanced to be surprised by some hunters, and had much ado to get off. However, she did not forget her favourite young one, which she took up in her arms that it might be the more secure; the other, which she neglected, by natural instinct, leaped upon her back, and so away they scampered together. But it unluckily fell out that the mother, in her hurried flight, blinded with haste, dashed her favourite's head against a stone and killed it. The hated one, clinging close to her rough back, escaped all the danger of the pursuit.

FAVOURITISM IS NOT KINDNESS.

THE SENSIBLE ASS

An old fellow was feeding an Ass in a fine green meadow, and, being alarmed with the sudden approach of the enemy, was impatient with the Ass to put himself forward and fly with all the speed that he was able. The Ass asked him whether or not he thought the enemy would clap two pair of panniers upon his back.

The man said:

"No, there was no fear of that."

"Why, then," said the Ass, "I will not stir an inch, for what is it to me who my master is, since I shall but carry my panniers as usual?"

THE MASTER AND HIS SCHOLAR

As a Schoolmaster was walking upon the bank of a river not far from his school, he heard a cry as of one in distress; advancing a few paces farther, he saw one of his scholars in the water, hanging by the bough of a willow. The boy had, it seems, been learning to swim with corks; and, now thinking himself sufficiently experienced, had thrown those implements aside and ventured into the water without them, but the force of the stream having hurried him out of his depth, he had certainly been drowned had not the branch of a willow, which grew on the bank, providentially hung in his way. The Master took up the corks which lay upon the ground, and, throwing them to his Scholar, made use of this opportunity to read a lecture to him upon the inconsiderate rashness of youth.

"Let this be an example to you," says he, "in the conduct of your future life, never to throw away your corks till time has given you strength and experience enough to swim without them."

DON'T START UNTIL YOU ARE READY.

THE FROG
AND THE FOX

A FROG leaping out of a lake, and taking the advantage of a rising ground, made proclamation to all beasts of the forest that he was an able physician, and, for curing all manner of illnesses, would turn his back to no person living. This discourse, uttered in a set of harsh words, which nobody understood, made the beasts admire his learning, and give credit to everything he said. At last, a Fox, who was present, with indignation asked him how he could have the impudence, with those thin lantern jaws, that meagre pale face and blotched, spotted body, to set up for one who was able to cure the infirmities of others.

THE HEN AND THE FOX

A Fox having crept into an outhouse looked up and down, seeking what he might devour, and at last spied a Hen sitting upon the uppermost perch, so high that he could by no means come at her. He then had recourse to his old stratagem.

" Dear Cousin," says he, addressing himself to the Hen, "how do you do? I heard that you were ill, and kept within; at which I was so concerned, that I could not rest till I came to see you. Pray, how is it with you now? Let me feel your pulse a little, indeed, you do not look well at all."

He was running on after this impudent, fulsome manner when the Hen answered him from the roost :

" Truly, Cousin Reynard, you are right. I never was in more pain in my life. I must beg your pardon for being so free as to tell you, that I see no company ; and you must excuse me, too, for not coming down to you, for, to say the truth, my condition is such that I fear I should catch my death if I should do it."

THE COCK AND
THE FOX

A Fox passing early one summer's morning near
a farmyard was caught in a spring, which a farmer
had planted there for that purpose. A Cock
at a distance saw what happened, and, hardly yet
daring to trust himself too near so dangerous a
foe, approached him cautiously and peeped at
him, not without some horror and dread of mind.
Reynard no sooner perceived it but he addressed
himself to him with all the designing artifice
imaginable.

"Dear Cousin," says he, "you see what an un-
fortunate accident has befallen me here, and all
upon your account. For, as I was creeping
through yonder hedge in my way homeward I
heard you crow, and was resolved to ask you how

you did before I went any further, but by the way I met with this disaster, and therefore now I must become a humble suitor to you for a knife to cut this plaguy string, or, at least, that you would conceal my misfortune till I have gnawed it asunder with my teeth."

The Cock, seeing how the case stood, made no reply, but posted away as fast as he could, and gave the farmer an account of the whole matter, who, taking a good weapon along with him, came and did the Fox's business before he could have time to contrive his escape.

DEVOTE YOUR COMPASSION TO SUITABLE OBJECTS.

THE WIND AND THE SUN

A DISPUTE once arose betwixt the North-wind and the Sun, about the superiority of their power; and they agreed to try their strength upon a traveller, which should be able to get his cloak off first. The North-wind began, and blew a very cold blast, accompanied with a sharp driving shower. But this, and whatever else he

could do, instead of making the man quit his
cloak, obliged him to gird it about his body as
close as possible.

Next came the Sun, who, breaking out from a
thick watery cloud, drove away the cold vapours
from the sky, and darted his warm sultry beams
upon the head of the poor weather-beaten
traveller. The man, growing faint with the
heat, and unable to endure it any longer, first
threw off his heavy cloak, and then hurried for
protection to the shade of a neighbouring grove.

PERSUASION IS BETTER THAN FORCE.

THE YOUNG MAN & THE LION

THERE was a certain old man who was lord of a very great estate, and had only one child, a son, of whom he was exceedingly fond ; he was likewise one very apt to be influenced by omens and dreams. The young Man, his son, was mightily addicted to hunting, and used to be up early every morning to follow the chase. But the father happening to dream one night that his son was killed by a Lion, took it so to heart, that he would not suffer him to go into the forest any more. He built a fine castle for his reception, in which he kept him close confined, lest he should step out privately a-hunting and meet his fate. Yet as this was purely the effect of his love and fondness for him, he studied to make his confinement as agreeable to him as possible, and, in order to do so he furnished the castle with a variety of fine pictures, in which were all sorts of wild beasts, such as the son used to take a delight in hunting, and, among the rest, the portrait of a Lion. This the young man viewed one day more attentively than usual, and, being vexed in his mind at the unreasonable confinement which his father's dream had occasioned, he broke out into a violent passion, and, looking sternly at the Lion:

"Thou cruel savage," says he, "it is to thy grim and terrible form that I owe my imprisonment, if I had a sword in my hand I would thus run it through thy heart."

Saying this he struck his fist at the Lion's breast, and unfortunately tore his hand with a point of a nail which stuck in the wainscot, and was hid under the canvas. The wound festered and turned to a gangrene; this threw the young man into a fever, and he died. So that the father's dream was fulfilled by the very caution that he took to prevent it!

FATE CANNOT BE OUTWITTED.

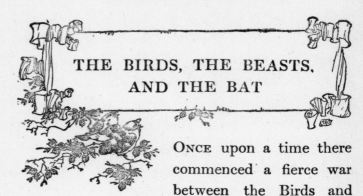

THE BIRDS, THE BEASTS, AND THE BAT

ONCE upon a time there commenced a fierce war between the Birds and the Beasts, when the Bat taking advantage of the fact that he was something between a bird and a beast, hoped by that means to live secure in a state of neutrality, and save his bacon. It was not long before the forces on each side met and gave battle, and their animosities running very high, a bloody slaughter ensued. The Bat, at the beginning of the day, thinking the Birds most likely to carry it, listed himself among them; but kept fluttering at a little distance, that he might the better observe and take his measures accordingly. However, after some time spent in the action, the army of the Beasts seeming to prevail, he went entirely over to them, and endeavoured to convince them

THE BIRDS, BEASTS, AND BAT

by the affinity which he had to a Mouse that he was by nature a Beast, and would always continue firm and true to their interest. His plea was admitted; but in the end, the advantage turning completely on the side of the Birds under the admirable conduct and courage of their general, the Eagle, the Bat, to save his life and escape the disgrace of falling into the hands of his deserted friends, betook himself to flight. And ever since, skulking in caves and hollow trees all day, as if ashamed to show himself, he never appears till the dusk of the evening, when all the feathered inhabitants of the air are gone to roost.

DON'T CHANGE SIDES MORE THAN ONCE.

THE FOWLER AND THE LARK

A FOWLER set snares to catch Larks in the open field. A Lark was caught, and, finding herself entangled, could not help lamenting her hard fate.

"Ah, woe is me!" says she. "What crime have I committed? I have taken neither silver nor gold, nor anything of value, but must die only for eating a poor grain of wheat."

THE ANT AND THE GRASSHOPPER

In the winter season a commonwealth of Ants was busily employed in the management and preservation of their corn, which they exposed to the air in heaps round about the avenues of their little country habitation. A Grasshopper, who had chanced to outlive the summer, and was ready to starve with cold and hunger, approached them with great humility, and begged that they would relieve his necessity with one grain of wheat or rye. One of the Ants asked him how he had spent his time in summer, that he had not taken the trouble to lay in a stock, as they had done ?

"Alas! gentlemen," says he, "I passed away the time merrily and pleasantly in drinking, singing, and dancing, and never once thought of winter."

"If that be the case," replied the Ant, laughing, "all I have to say is that they who drink, sing, and dance in the summer, must starve in the winter."

IN PROSPEROUS TIMES DO NOT FORGET THAT BAD
TIMES MAY COME.

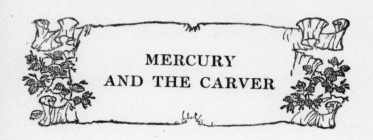

MERCURY
AND THE CARVER

MERCURY, having a mind to know how much he was esteemed among men, transformed himself into the shape of one of them, and going into a carver's shop where little images were to be sold, he saw Jupiter, Juno, himself, and most of the other gods and goddesses. So pretending that he wanted to buy, says he to the Carver :

"What do you ask for this?" and pointing to the figure of Jupiter.

"A groat," says the other.

"And what for that?" meaning Juno.

"I must have something more for that," says he.

"Well, and what's the price of this?" says Mercury, nodding his head at himself.

"Why," says the Man, "if you are in earnest and will buy the other two, I will throw you that into the bargain."

DON'T INQUIRE AFTER YOUR OWN WORTH.

THE LION AND THE FOUR BULLS

FOUR Bulls which had entered into a very close friendship kept always near one another, and fed together. A Lion often saw them, and as often had a mind to make one of them his prey; but though he could easily have subdued any of them singly, yet he was afraid to attack the whole alliance, as knowing they would have been too much for him, and therefore contented himself for the present with keeping at a distance. At last, perceiving no attempt was to be made upon them as long as this combination held, he took occasion, by hints or whispers, to foment jealousies and raise divisions among them. This stratagem succeeded so well that the Bulls grew cold and reserved towards one another, which soon after ripened into a downright hatred, and at last ended in a total separation. The Lion had now obtained his ends; and, as impossible as it was for him to hurt them while they were united, he found no difficulty, now they were parted, in seizing and devouring every one of the four Bulls, one after another.

UNITY IS STRENGTH.

THE CAT AND THE FOX

ONCE upon a time as the Cat and the Fox were talking politics together, in the middle of a forest, Reynard said, " Let things turn out ever so bad, he did not care, for he had a thousand tricks for them yet, before they should hurt him. But pray," says he, " Mrs. Puss, suppose there should be an invasion, what course do you design to take ?"

" Nay," says the Cat, " I have but one shift for it, and if that won't do, I am undone."

" I am sorry for you," replies Reynard, " with all my heart, and would gladly furnish you with one or two of mine. But indeed, neighbour, as times go, it is not good to trust ; we must even be every one for himself, as the saying is, and so your humble servant."

These words were scarcely out of his mouth

when they were alarmed with a pack of hounds, that came upon them in full cry. The Cat, by the help of her single shift, ran up a tree, and sat securely among the top branches; from whence she beheld Reynard, who had not been able to get out of sight, overtaken with his thousand tricks, and torn in as many pieces by the Dogs which had surrounded him.

SOME FOLK ARE TOO CUNNING.

THE MAN AND HIS GOOSE

A CERTAIN Man had a Goose which laid him a golden egg every day. But, not contented with this, which rather increased than abated his avarice, he was resolved to kill the Goose, and cut her up that so he might come to the inexhaustible treasure which he fancied she had within her. He did so, and, to his great sorrow and disappointment, found nothing.

THE GREEDY OFTEN OVERREACH THEMSELVES.

JUPITER AND
THE ASS

A CERTAIN Ass which belonged to a gardener,
and was weary of carrying his heavy burdens,
prayed to Jupiter to give him a new master;
Jupiter, consenting to his petition, gave him a
tile-maker, who loaded him with tiles and made
him carry heavier burdens than before. Again
he came and made supplications, beseeching the
god to give him one that was more mild, or, at
least, to let him have any other master but this.
Jupiter could not help laughing at his folly; however, he granted his request this time also, and
made him over to a tanner. But as soon as the
poor Ass discovered what a master he had got,
he could not help blaming himself for his great

folly and inconstancy, which had brought him to a master not only more cruel and exacting than either of the former, but one that would not spare his very hide after he was dead.

A CHANGE MAY BE FOR THE WORSE.

THE TORTOISE AND THE EAGLE

A TORTOISE, weary of his condition, by which he was confined to creep upon the ground, and being ambitious to have a prospect, and look about him, gave out that if any bird would take him up into the air, and show him the world, he would reward him with a discovery of many precious stones, which he knew were hidden in a certain place of the earth. The Eagle undertook to do as he desired, and when he had performed his commission, demanded the reward. But finding the Tortoise could not make good his words, he stuck his talons into the softer parts of his body, and made him a sacrifice to his revenge.

IT IS UNWISE TO ACCEPT A FAVOUR FROM AN ENEMY.

THE FOX
AND THE CROW

A Crow having taken a piece of cheese out of a cottage window, flew up into a high tree with it in order to eat it, which the Fox observing, came and sat underneath, and began to compliment the Crow upon the subject of her beauty.

"I protest," says he, "I never observed it before. but your feathers are of a more delicate white than any that ever I saw in my life. Ah, what a fine shape and graceful turn of body is there! And I make no question but you have a tolerable voice. If it is but as fine as your complexion, I do not know a bird that can pretend to stand in competition with you."

The Crow, tickled with this very civil language, nestled and wriggled about, and hardly knew

where she was ; but, thinking the Fox a little
dubious as to the exact tones of her voice, and
having a mind to set him right in that matter,
began to sing, and in the same instant let the
cheese drop out of her mouth. This being what
the Fox wanted he chopped it up in a moment,
and trotted away, laughing to himself at the
easy credulity of the Crow.

BEWARE OF THE FLATTERING TONGUE.

THE PEACOCK AND THE CRANE

A PEACOCK and a Crane by chance met together
in the same place. The Peacock, erecting his
tail, displayed his gaudy plumes, and looked
with contempt upon the Crane, as some mean
ordinary person. The Crane, resolving to
mortify his insolence, took occasion to say that
Peacocks were very fine birds indeed, if fine
feathers could make them so, but that he
thought it a much nobler thing to be able to rise
above the clouds than to strut about upon the
ground, and be gazed at by children.

DO NOT COMMENT ON THE LACK IN OTHERS OF THE
QUALITIES YOU POSSESS.

THE LION IN LOVE

A LION by chance saw a fair maid, the Forester's daughter, as she was tripping over a lawn, and fell in love with her. Nay, so violent was his passion that he could not live unless he made her his own; so that without any more delay, he broke his mind to the father, and demanded the damsel for his wife. The man, as odd as the proposal seemed at first, yet soon recollected that by agreeing he might get the Lion into his power; but, by refusing him, should only exasperate and provoke his rage. Therefore he consented, but told him it must be upon these conditions: that, considering the girl was young and tender, he must agree to let his teeth be plucked out and his claws cut off, lest he should hurt her, or at least frighten her with the apprehension of them. The Lion was too much in love to hesitate, but was no sooner deprived of his teeth and claws than the treacherous Forester attacked him with a huge club, and knocked his brains out.

THE FIERCEST CAN BE TAMED BY LOVE.

THE SOW AND THE WOLF

A Sow lay in a sty with her whole litter of pigs about her. A Wolf, who longed for one of them, but knew not how to come at it, endeavoured to insinuate himself into the Sow's good opinion. And, accordingly, coming up to her :

" How does the good woman of the straw do?" says he. " Can I be of any service to you, Mrs. Sow, in relation to your little family here? If you have a mind to go abroad and air yourself a little, you may depend upon it I will take as much care of your Pigs as you could do yourself."

" Your humble servant," says the Sow, " I thoroughly understand your meaning ; and, to let you know I do, I must be so free as to tell you I had rather have your room than your company, and, therefore, if you would act like a Wolf of honour and oblige me, I beg I may never see your face again."

DO NOT ACCEPT FAVOURS FROM THE UNTRUSTWORTHY.

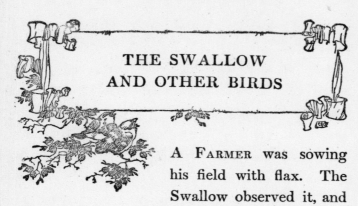

THE SWALLOW
AND OTHER BIRDS

A FARMER was sowing his field with flax. The Swallow observed it, and desired the other birds to assist her in picking the seed up and destroying it, telling them that flax was that evil material of which the thread was composed which made the fowler's nets, and by that means contributed to the ruin of so many innocent birds. But the poor Swallow, not having the good fortune to be regarded, the flax sprang up and appeared above the ground. She then put them in mind once more of their impending danger, and wished them to pluck it up in the bud before it went any farther. They still neglected her warnings, and the flax grew up into the high stalk. She yet again desired them to attack it, as it was not yet too late. But all that she could get was to be ridiculed and despised for a silly, pretending prophet. The Swallow, finding all her remonstrances availed nothing, was resolved to leave the society of such unthinking, careless creatures before it was too late. So, quitting the woods, she repaired to the houses, and forsaking the conversation of the birds, has ever since made her abode among the dwellings of men.

ATTACK AN EVIL BEFORE ITS SEEDS HAVE GROWN.

THE HORSE AND THE STAG

THE Stag, with his sharp horns, got the better of the Horse, and drove him clear out of the pasture where they used to feed together. So the latter craved the assistance of man, and, in order to receive the benefit of it, suffered him to put a bridle into his mouth and a saddle upon his back. By this way of proceeding he entirely defeated his enemy, but was mightily disappointed when, upon returning thanks and desiring to be dismissed, he received this answer:

"No; I never knew before how useful a drudge you were; now I have found what you are good for, you may depend upon it I will keep you to it."

THE LION AND THE MOUSE

A Lion, faint with heat and weary with hunting,
lay down to take his repose under the spreading
boughs of a thick shady oak. It happened that
while he slept, a company of scrambling Mice
ran over his back and awoke him. Upon which,
starting up, he clapped his paw upon one of them,
and was just going to put it to death when the
little supplicant implored his mercy in a very
moving manner, begging him not to stain his
noble character with the blood of so despicable
and small a beast. The Lion, considering the
matter, thought proper to do as he was desired,
and immediately released his little trembling
prisoner. Not long after, traversing the forest in

pursuit of his prey, he chanced to run into a net fixed by some hunters; from whence not being able to disengage himself, he set up a most hideous and loud roar. The Mouse, hearing the voice, and knowing it to be the Lion's, immediately repaired to the place and bid him fear nothing, for that he was his friend. Then straight he fell to work, and with his sharp little teeth gnawing asunder the knots and fastenings of the net, set the royal brute at liberty.

A LITTLE FRIEND IS NOT TO BE DESPISED.

THE FATAL MARRIAGE

THE Lion aforesaid, touched with the grateful procedure of the Mouse, and resolving not to be outdone in generosity by any wild beast whatsoever, desired his little deliverer to name his own terms, saying that he might depend upon his agreeing to any proposal he should make. The Mouse, fired with ambition at this gracious offer, did not so much consider what was proper for him to ask as what was in the power of the Lion to grant, and so presumptuously demanded his princely daughter, the young Lioness, in marriage. The Lion consented; but when he would have given the royal virgin into his possession, she being a careless young thing, not minding how she walked, by chance put her paw upon the bridegroom, who was coming to meet her, and crushed the little thing to pieces.

DO NOT ASK FOR THE IMPOSSIBLE.

THE TWO POTS

AN Earthen Pot, and one of Brass, standing together upon the river's brink, were both carried away by the flowing in of the tide. The Earthen Pot showed some uneasiness, as fearing he should be broken; but his companion of Brass bid him be under no apprehension, for that he would take care of him.

"Oh," replies the other, "keep as far off as ever you can, I entreat you; it is of you I am most afraid: for, whether the stream dashes you against me, or me against you, I am sure to be the sufferer; and therefore I beg of you do not let us come near one another."

THE HARE AND THE TORTOISE

A Hare insulted a Tortoise upon account of his slowness, and vainly boasted of his own great speed in running.

"Let us make a match," replied the Tortoise. "I'll run with you five miles for five pounds, and the Fox yonder shall be the umpire of the race."

The Hare agreed, and away they both started together. But the Hare, by reason of his exceeding swiftness, outran the Tortoise to such a degree that he made a jest of the matter, and finding himself a little tired, squatted in a tuft of fern that grew by the way and took a nap; thinking, that if the Tortoise went by, he could at any time catch him up with all the ease imaginable. In the meanwhile the Tortoise came jogging on with a slow but continued motion, and the Hare, out of a too great security and confidence of victory, oversleeping himself, the Tortoise arrived at the end of the race first.

KEEPING ON WINS THE RACE.

THE HARE AND THE TORTOISE

"The Hare . over-sleeping himself, the Tortoise arrived at the end of the race first."

THE LION, THE BEAR, AND THE FOX

A Lion and a Bear having fallen out over the
carcass of a Fawn, which they found in the
forest, they decided that their right to him
should be settled by force of arms. The battle
was severe and tough on both sides, and they
held it out, tearing and worrying one another so
long that, what with wounds and fatigue, they
were so faint and weary, they were not able to
strike another stroke. Thus, while they lay
upon the ground, panting and lolling out their
tongues, a Fox chanced to pass by that way,
who, seeing how the case stood, very impudently
stepped in between them, seized the booty which
they had all this while been contending for, and
carried it off. The two combatants, who lay
and beheld all this, without having strength

enough to stir and prevent it, were only wise enough to make this reflection:

" Behold the fruits of our strife and contention ! That villain, the Fox, bears away the prize, and we ourselves have taken from each other the power to get it back from him.

RATHER DIVIDE THE SPOIL THAN FIGHT OVER IT.

JUPITER AND THE CAMEL

A CAMEL presented a petition to Jupiter, complaining of the hardship of his case, in not having, like bulls and other creatures, horns, or any weapons of defence to protect himself from the attacks of his enemies; and praying that relief might be given him in such manner as might be thought most expedient. Jupiter could not help smiling at the impertinent address of the great silly beast ; but, however, he rejected the petition, and told him that, so far from granting his unreasonable request, henceforward he would take care his ears should be shortened, as a punishment for his presumptuous request.

BE CONTENT WITH YOUR LOT.

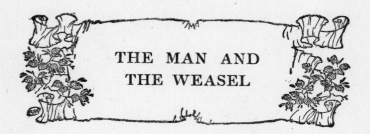

THE MAN AND
THE WEASEL

A MAN had caught a Weasel, and was just going
to kill it. The poor creature, to escape death,
cried out in a pitiful manner:

"Oh, pray, do not kill me, for I am useful to
you and keep your house clear from mice."

"Why, truly," says the man, "if I thought
you did it purely out of love to me I should not
only be inclined to pardon you, but think myself
mightily obliged to you. But whereas you not
only kill them, but yourself do the same mischief
they would do in eating and gnawing my victuals,
I desire you would place your insignificant ser-
vices to some other account, and not to mine."

Having said this, he took the wicked vermin
and strangled it immediately.

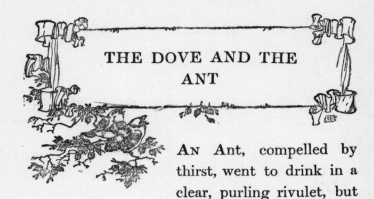

THE DOVE AND THE ANT

An Ant, compelled by thirst, went to drink in a clear, purling rivulet, but the current, with its circling eddy, snatched her away and carried her down the stream. A Dove, pitying her distressed condition, cropped a branch from a neighbouring tree and let it fall into the water, by means of which the Ant saved herself and got ashore. Not long after a Fowler having a design against the Dove, planted his nets in due order without the bird's observing what he was about, which the Ant perceiving just as he was going to put his design into execution, she bit him by the heel and made him give so sudden a start, that the Dove took the alarm and flew away.

ONE GOOD TURN DESERVES ANOTHER.

THE WOLF &
THE LAMB

ONE hot, sultry day, a Wolf and a Lamb happened to come just at the same time to quench their thirst in the stream of a clear silver brook that ran tumbling down the side of a rocky mountain. The Wolf stood upon the higher ground, and the Lamb at some distance from him down the current. However, the Wolf, having a mind to pick a quarrel with him, asked him what he meant by disturbing the water, and making it so muddy that he could not drink, and at the same time demanded satisfaction. The Lamb, frightened at this threatening charge, told him, in a tone as mild as possible, that with humble submission he could not conceive how that could be, since the water which he drank ran down from the Wolf to him, and therefore it could not be disturbed so far up the stream.

"Be that as it will," replies the Wolf; "you are a rascal, and I have been told that you treated me with ill language behind my back about half a year ago."

"Upon my word," says the Lamb, "the time you mention was before I was born."

The Wolf, finding it to no purpose to argue any longer against truth, fell into a great passion, snarling and foaming at the mouth as if he had been mad, and drawing nearer to the Lamb.

"Sirrah," says he, "if it was not you it was your father, and that's all one."

So he seized the poor, innocent, helpless thing tore it to pieces, and made a meal of it.

A TYRANT DOES NOT TROUBLE TO JUSTIFY HIS EXCUSES.

THE FORESTER AND THE LION

A FORESTER meeting with a Lion one day, they talked together for a while without differing much in opinion. At last a dispute happening to arise about the point of superiority between a man and a Lion, the man, wanting better argument, showed the Lion a marble monument, on which was placed the statue of a man striding over a vanquished Lion.

" If this," says the Lion, " is all you have to say for it, let us be the carvers, and we will make the Lion striding over the Man."

EACH SIDE PICTURES THINGS AS THEY WOULD LIKE THEM TO BE.

THE MOUSE AND THE WEASEL

A LITTLE, starveling, thin rogue of a Mouse had with much pushing application made his way through a small hole in a corn basket, where he stuffed and crammed so plentifully that when he would have retired the way he came, he found himself too plump, with all his endeavours, to accomplish it. A Weasel, who stood at some distance, and had been amusing himself with beholding the vain efforts of the little fat thing, called to him, and said :

" Harkee ! Honest friend, if you have a mind to make your escape, there is but one way for it; contrive to grow as poor and as lean as you were when you entered, and then perhaps you may get off."

THE FOX AND THE TIGER

A SKILFUL archer, coming into the woods, shot his arrows so successfully that he slew many wild beasts, and pursued several others. This put the whole savage kind into a dreadful state of fear, and made them fly to the most retired thickets for refuge. At last, a Tiger took courage, and, bidding them not to be afraid, said that he alone would engage the enemy, telling them they might depend upon his valour and strength to revenge their wrongs. In the midst of these threats, while he was lashing himself with his tail, and tearing up the ground for anger, an arrow pierced his ribs, and hung by its barbed point in his side. He set up a hideous and loud roar, caused by the pain which he felt, and endeavoured to draw out the painful dart

THE FOWLER AND THE BLACKBIRD

with his teeth, when a Fox, approaching him, inquired with an air of surprise, who it was that could have strength and courage enough to wound so mighty and valorous a beast!

"Ah!" says the Tiger, "I was mistaken in my reckoning: it was that invincible man yonder."

COURAGE WITHOUT RESOURCE DOES NOT ALWAYS WIN.

THE FOWLER AND THE BLACKBIRD

A FOWLER was placing his nets and putting his tackle in order by the side of a copse, when a Blackbird, who saw him, had the curiosity to inquire what he was doing. Says he:

"I am building a city for you birds to live in, and providing it with meat, and all manner of conveniences for you."

Having said this, he departed and hid himself; and the Blackbird, believing the words, came into the nets, and was taken. But when the man came up to take hold of him:

"If this," says he, "be your faith and honesty, and these the cities you build, I am of opinion you will have but few inhabitants."

DECEIVERS ARE SOON FOUND OUT.

THE FROG AND
THE MOUSE

THERE was once a great contest between the
Frog and the Mouse which should be master of
the fen, and war ensued upon the matter. But
the crafty Mouse, lurking under the grass in
ambuscade, made sudden sallies and often surprised the enemy at a disadvantage. The Frog,
excelling in strength, and being more able to leap
abroad and take the field, challenged the Mouse
to single combat. The Mouse accepted the
challenge, and each of them entered the lists,
armed with the point of a bulrush instead of a
spear. A Kite, sailing in the air, beheld them
afar off, and while they were eagerly bent upon
each other and pressing on to the duel this fatal
enemy descended suddenly upon them, and, with
her crooked talons, carried off both the champions.

THE BOAR AND THE ASS

A LITTLE scoundrel of an Ass, happening to meet with a Boar, had a mind to be waggish with him:

"And so, brother," says he, "your humble servant."

The Boar, somewhat nettled at his familiarity, bristled up to him, and told him he was surprised to hear him utter so impudent an untruth, and was just going to show his noble resentment by giving him a rip in the flank, but, wisely stifling his passion, he contented himself with only saying:

"Go, you sorry beast! I could be amply and easily revenged of you, but I don't care to foul my tusks with the blood of so base a creature."

THE COCK AND
THE FOX

A Cock being perched among the branches of a lofty tree, crowed aloud, so that the shrillness of his voice echoed through the wood and invited a Fox to the place, who was prowling in that neighbourhood in quest of his prey. But Reynard, finding that the Cock could not be reached because of the height of his position, had recourse to stratagem in order to decoy him down, so, approaching the tree:

"Cousin," says he, "I am heartily glad to see you, but at the same time I cannot help expressing my uneasiness at the inconvenience of the place, which will not let me pay my respects to you in a more handsome manner, though I suppose you will come down presently, and so that difficulty is easily removed."

THE COCK AND THE FOX

"Indeed, Cousin," says the Cock, "to tell you the truth, I do not think it safe to venture upon the ground; for though I am convinced how much you are my friend, yet I may have the misfortune to fall into the clutches of some other beast, and what will become of me then?"

"Oh, dear," says Reynard, "is it possible that you can be so ignorant as not to know of the peace that has been lately proclaimed between all kinds of birds and beasts; and that we are for the future to cease hostilities on all sides and to live in the utmost love and harmony, and that under penalty of suffering the severest punishment that can be inflicted?"

All this while the Cock seemed to give little attention to what was said, but stretched out his neck, as if he saw something at a distance.

"Cousin," says the Fox, "what is that you look at so earnestly?"

"Why," says the Cock, "I think I see a pack of Hounds yonder, a little way off."

"Oh, then," says the Fox, "your humble servant, I must be gone."

"Nay; pray, Cousin, do not go," said the

Cock, " I am just coming down, sure you are not afraid of Dogs in these peaceable times."

" No, no !" said he, " but it is ten to one whether they have heard of the proclamation yet."

IT IS WELL TO TEST THE STATEMENTS OF THE CRAFTY.

THE CROW AND THE PITCHER

A CROW, ready to die with thirst, flew with joy to a Pitcher, which he beheld at some distance. When he came, he found water in it indeed, but so near the bottom that with all his stooping and straining he was not able to reach it. Then he tried to overturn the Pitcher, that so at least he might be able to get a little of it. But his strength was not sufficient for this. At last seeing some pebbles lie near the place, he cast them one by one into the Pitcher, and thus, by degrees, raised the water up to the very brim, and satisfied his thirst.

AN END CAN BE ACCOMPLISHED IN MORE THAN ONE WAY.

THE JUDICIOUS LION

A Lion having taken a young Bullock, stood over, and was going to devour it, when a thief stepped in and cried halves with him.

" No, friend," says the Lion ; " you are too apt to take what is not your due, and therefore I shall have nothing to say to you."

By chance a poor, honest traveller happened to come that way, and, seeing the Lion, modestly and timorously withdrew, intending to go another way ; upon which the generous beast, with a courteous, affable behaviour desired him to come forward, and partake with him in that to which his modesty and humility had given him so good a title. Then, dividing the prey into two equal parts and feasting himself upon one of them, he retired into the woods, and left the place clear for the honest man to come in for his share.

BEWARE OF GIVING FAVOURS BECAUSE OF IMPORTUNITY.

THE MAN AND HIS TWO WIVES

A MAN, in times when it was the custom to
have more than one wife, had two; one ot whom,
like himself, had seen her best days, and was
just, as it were, entering upon the downward
path of life. But this, being an artful woman,
she entirely concealed by her dress, by which and
some other elegant qualities she made a shift
sometimes to engage her husband's heart. The
other was a beautiful young creature of seven-
teen, whose charms, as yet in the height of bloom
and secure of their own power, had no occasion
to call in any artifice to their assistance. She
made the good man as happy as he was capable
of being, but was not, it seems, completely so
herself; the grey hairs mixed among the black
upon her husband's head gave her some uneasiness by proclaiming the great difference of
their ages. Wherefore, under colour of adjust-
ing and combing his head, she would every now
and then snip out a few silver hairs with her
scissors; that, however matters were, he might
still have as few visible signs of an advanced age

as possible. The dame whose years were nearer to an equality with his own esteemed those grey locks as the honours of his head, and could have wished they had all been such. She thought it gave him a dignified look. At least, that it made her appear something younger than he, so that every time the honest man's head fell into her hands she took as much pains to get rid of the black hairs as the other had done to demolish the grey. They neither of them knew of the other's design ; but each continuing her project with great industry, the poor man, who thought their desire to please him made them so anxious to attend to his head, found himself, in a short time, without any hair at all !

THE HUSBANDMAN AND HIS SONS

A CERTAIN Husbandman, lying at the point of death, and desiring his Sons to pursue that innocent, entertaining life of agriculture, in which himself had been engaged all his life, made use of this plan to induce them to keep to it. He called them to his bedside, and spoke to this effect.

" All the patrimony I have to bequeath to you, Sons, is my farm and my vineyard, of which I make you joint heirs. But I charge you not to let it go out of your own occupation: for, if I have any treasure besides, it lies buried somewhere in the ground, within a foot of the surface."

This made the Sons conclude that he talked of money which he had hid there: so, after their father's death, with unwearied diligence and application, they carefully dug up every inch, both of the farm and vineyard. From which it came to pass, that though they missed the treasure which they expected, the ground by being so well stirred and loosened, produced such plentiful crops of all that was sowed in it, that it proved a real, and no inconsiderable treasure.

INDUSTRY BRINGS ITS OWN REWARD.

THE MAN AND THE GNAT

As a clownish fellow was sitting on a bank a Gnat settled upon his leg and stung it. He clapped his hand with great vehemence upon the place, with intention to kill the Gnat, but the little nimble insect, skipping lightly between his fingers, escaped; and every time he struck he gave himself a smart blow upon the leg, without being in the least able to touch the Gnat. This provoked him very much, so that in the height of his passion he fell to invoking Hercules.

"O mighty Hercules," says he, "since nothing can withstand thy power, aid me, I beseech thee, against this pernicious Gnat, and with thy invincible strength subdue him in compassion to me, miserable creature, who am tormented with his venomous sting."

YOU MAY INJURE YOURSELF IN ATTACKING A DESPICABLE ENEMY.

THE ASS, THE LION, AND THE COCK

AN Ass and a Cock happened to be feeding together in the same place, when suddenly they spied a Lion approaching them. This beast is reported, above all things, to have a dislike, or rather antipathy, to the crowing of a Cock, so that he no sooner heard the voice of that bird but he took to his heels, and ran away as fast as ever he could. The Ass, fancying he fled for fear of him, in the bravery of his heart pursued him, and followed him so far that they were quite out of hearing of the Cock, which the Lion no sooner perceived but he turned about and seized the Ass, and just as he was ready to tear him to pieces, the sluggish creature is said to have expressed himself thus:

THE FISHERMAN

" Alas ! fool that I was, knowing the cowardice of my own nature, thus by an affected courage to throw myself into the jaws of death when I might have remained secure and unmolested."

THE FISHERMAN

A CERTAIN Fisherman having laid his nets in the river and encompassed the whole stream from one side to the other, took a long pole and fell a beating the water, to make the fish strike into his nets. One of the neighbours that lived thereabouts seeing him do so, wondered what he meant, and, going up to him :

" Friend," says he, " what are you doing here ? Do you think it is to be suffered that you shall stand splashing and dashing the water, and make it so muddy that it is not fit for use ? Who do you think can live at this rate ?"

He was going on in a great fury when the other interrupted him, and replied :

" I do not much trouble myself how you are to live with my doing this, but I assure you that I cannot live without it."

LIVE AND LET LIVE.

101

THE FOX AND THE COUNTRYMAN

A Fox being hard hunted, and having run a
long way, was quite tired; at last he spied a
country fellow in a wood, to whom he applied
for refuge, entreating that he would give him
leave to hide himself in his cottage till the
hounds were gone by. The Man consented, and
the Fox went and covered himself up close in a
corner of the hovel. Presently the hunters came
up, and inquired of the Man if he had seen the
Fox.

" No," says he, " I have not seen him indeed."
But all the while he pointed with his finger to
the place where the Fox was hid. However, the
hunters did not understand him, but called off
their hounds and went another way. Soon after
the Fox, creeping out of his hole, was going to
sneak off, when the Man, calling after him, asked
him if that was his manners to go away without
thanking his benefactor, to whose fidelity he
owed his life. Reynard, who had peeped all the
while and seen what passed, answered :

" I know what obligations I have to you well
enough ; and, I assure you, if your actions had

but been agreeable to your words I should have
endeavoured, however incapable of it, to have
returned you suitable thanks."

THE HORSE
AND THE ASS

A Horse, adorned with his great war-saddle and
champing his foaming bridle, came thundering
along the way, and made the mountains echo with
his loud, shrill neighing.   He had not gone far
before he overtook an Ass, who was labouring
under a heavy burden and moving slowly on in
the same track with himself.   Immediately he
called out to him in a haughty, imperious tone,
and threatened to trample him in the dirt if he
did not make way for him.   The poor, patient

Ass, not daring to dispute the matter, quietly got out of his way as fast as he could and let him go by. Not long after this the same Horse in an engagement with the enemy happened to be shot in the eye, which made him unfit for show or any military business, so he was stripped of his fine ornaments and sold to a carrier. The Ass, meeting him in this forlorn condition, thought that now it was his time to insult.

" And so," says he, " Heyday, friend, is it you? Well, I always believed that pride of yours would one day have a fall."

THE FOX AND THE MASK

A Fox, being in a shop where masks were sold, laid his foot upon one of them, and, considering it awhile attentively, at last broke out into this exclamation:

" Bless me !" says he. " What a handsome goodly figure this makes ! What a pity it is that it should want brains !"

DO NOT BE DECEIVED BY OUTSIDE SHOW.

THE OLD WOMAN AND HER MAIDS

A CERTAIN Old Woman had several Maids, whom she used to call up to their work every morning at the crowing of the cock. The wenches, who found it grievous to have their sweet sleep disturbed so early, combined together and killed the cock, thinking that, when the alarm was gone, they might enjoy themselves in their warm beds a little longer. The Old Woman, grieved for the loss of her cock and having no means of telling the time, often called them in the middle of the night, so that they were more disturbed than they were when the cock was alive.

SMALL TROUBLES MAY BE EXCHANGED FOR WORSE ONES.

CÆSAR AND THE SLAVE

As Tiberius Cæsar was upon a progress to Naples once, he put in at a house he had upon the mountain Misenus, which was built there by Lucullus, and commanded a near view of the Tuscan Sea, having a distant prospect, even of that of Sicily. Here, as he was walking in the gardens and wildernesses, which were most delightfully green, one of his domestic slaves which belonged to that house, putting himself into a most alert posture and dress, appeared in one of the walks where the Emperor happened to be, sprinkling the ground with a watering-pot in order to lay the dust, and this he did so officiously that he was taken notice of and even laughed at, for he ran through private alleys and turnings, from one walk to another; so that wherever the Emperor went, he still found this fellow mightily busy with his watering-pot. But at last his design being discovered, which was, that he fancied Cæsar would be so touched with this diligence of his as to make him free; (part of which ceremony consisted in giving the Slave a gentle stroke on one side of his face), his imperial

THE SHEPHERD'S BOY

Majesty, being disposed to be merry, called him to him, and when the man came up, full of joyful expectation of his liberty:

" Hark, you, friend !" says he, "I have observed that you have been very busy a great while, but it was impertinently busy in officiously meddling where you had nothing to do while you might have employed your time better elsewhere; and, therefore, I must be so free as to tell you, that you have mistaken your man. I cannot afford a box on the ear at so low a price as you have bid for it."

THE SHEPHERD'S BOY

A CERTAIN Shepherd's boy who kept Sheep upon a common, in sport and wantonness would often cry out: " The Wolf, the Wolf!" By this means he several times drew the Husbandmen in an adjoining field from their work, who, finding themselves deluded, resolved for the future to take no notice of his alarm. Soon after the Wolf came indeed. The boy cried out in earnest. But no heed being given to his cries, the Sheep were devoured by the Wolf.

THOSE WHO TELL LIES FIND IT HARD TO BE BELIEVED WHEN THEY TELL THE TRUTH.

THE JACKDAW
& THE PIGEONS

A JACKDAW, observing that the Pigeons in a certain dovecot lived well and wanted for nothing, whitewashed his feathers, and, endeavouring to look as much like a dove as he could, went and lived among them. The Pigeons, not distinguishing him as long as he kept silent, forbore to give him any disturbance. But at last he forgot his character and began to chatter, by which the Pigeons, discovering what he was, flew upon him and beat him away from the meat, so that he was obliged to fly back to the Jackdaws again. They not knowing him in his discoloured feathers, drove him away likewise, so that he who had endeavoured to be more than he had a right to, was not permitted to be anything at all.

AN IMPOSTOR SOMETIMES OVERACTS HIS PART.

THE DOG INVITED TO SUPPER

A GENTLEMAN having invited a particular friend to sup with him, ordered a handsome entertainment to be prepared. His Dog observing this, thought with himself that now would be a good opportunity for him to invite another Dog, a friend of his, to partake of the good cheer. Accordingly he did so, and the strange Dog was conducted into the kitchen, where he saw mighty preparations going forward. Thought he to himself:

"This is rare! I shall fill myself charmingly by-and-by with some of these dainties. I'll eat enough to last me a week. Oh, how nicely and deliciously shall I feed."

While he stood and thought thus with himself his tail wagged and his mouth watered exceedingly, and this drew the observation of the cook towards him, who, seeing a strange cur with his eyes intent upon the victuals, stole softly behind him, and, taking him up by the two hind legs, threw him out of a window into the street. The hard stones gave him a very severe reception, and he was almost stunned with the fall; but recovering himself, he ran yelping and crying half the length of a street, the noise of which brought several other dogs about him, who, knowing of the invitation, began to inquire how he had fared.

" Oh," says he, " admirably well. I never was better entertained in my life ; but in truth, we drank a little too hard ; for my part, I was so overtaken that I scarcely know which way I got out of the house."

BE SURE YOUR INVITATION COMES FROM THE RIGHT QUARTER

THE GEESE AND THE CRANES

A FLOCK of Geese and a parcel of Cranes used often to feed together in a cornfield. At last the owner of the corn, with his servants, coming upon them of a sudden, surprised them in the very act, and the Geese being heavy, fat, full-bodied creatures, were most of them sufferers ; but the Cranes, being thin and light, easily flew away.

WEALTH WILL NOT ALWAYS SAVE A MAN.

THE DRUNKEN
HUSBAND

A CERTAIN Woman had a drunken Husband, upon whom, when she had endeavoured to re-claim several ways to no purpose, she tried this stratagem. When he was brought home one night dead drunk, as it seems he frequently used to be, she ordered him to be carried to a burial-place and there laid in a vault, as if he had been dead indeed. Thus she left him and went away, till she thought he might have come to himself and be sober again. When she returned and knocked at the door of the vault, the Man cried out:

" Who's there ?"

" I am the person," says she in a dismal tone, "that waits upon the dead folks, and I am come to bring you some victuals."

" Ah, good waiter," says he, " let the victuals alone and bring me a little drink, I beseech thee."

The Woman hearing this, fell a-tearing her hair and beating her breast in a woeful manner.

"Unhappy wretch that I am," says she; "this was the only way that I could think of to reform the wretched drunkard, but instead of gaining my point, I am only convinced that this drunkenness is an incurable habit, which he intends to carry with him into the other world."

BAD HABITS MAKE US SLAVES.

THE THIEF AND THE BOY

A Boy sat weeping upon the side of a well. A Thief, happening to come by just at the same time, asked him why he wept. The Boy, sighing and sobbing, replied, the string was broken and a silver tankard was fallen to the bottom of the well. Upon this the Thief pulled off his clothes, and went down into the well to look for it; where, having groped about a good while to no purpose, he came up again, but found neither his clothes nor the Boy, that little arch-dissembler having run away with them.

GULL A THIEF WHEN YOU CAN.

THE COUNTRY MOUSE AND THE CITY MOUSE

" ' Well,' says he, ' if this be your town life, much good may you do with it.' "

THE COUNTRY MOUSE AND THE CITY MOUSE

An honest, plain, sensible, country Mouse is said to have entertained at his hole one day a fine Mouse from the town. Having formerly been playfellows together, they were old acquaintances. which served as an apology for the visit. However, as master of the house, he thought himself obliged to do the honours of it in all respects, and to make as great a stranger of his guest as he possibly could. In order to do this he set before him a dish of delicate grey peas and bacon, another of fine oatmeal, some parings of new cheese; and, to crown all with a dessert, a remnant of a charming mellow apple. In good manners he forbore to eat any himself lest the stranger should not have enough, but that he might seem to bear the other company, sat and nibbled a piece of wheaten straw very busily. At last says the gay Mouse from the town:

"Old crony, give me leave to be a little free with you. How can you bear to live in this nasty, dirty, melancholy hole here, with nothing but woods, and meadows, and mountains, and rivulets about you? Do not you prefer the con-

versation of the world to the chirping of birds,
and the splendour of a court to the rude aspect
of an uncultivated desert ? Come, take my word
for it, you will find it a change for the better.
Never stand considering, but away this moment.
Remember we are not immortal, and therefore
have no time to lose. Make sure of to-day and
spend it as agreeably as you can, you know not
what may happen to-morrow."

In short, these and such like arguments prevailed, and his country acquaintance was resolved to go to town that night. So they both
set out upon their journey together, proposing
to sneak in after the close of the evening. They
did so, and about midnight made their entry into
a certain great house, where there had been an
extraordinary entertainment the day before, and
several tit-bits, which some of the servants had
purloined, were hid under the seat of a window ;
the country guest was immediately placed in the
midst of a rich Persian carpet. And now it was
the courtier's turn to entertain, who, indeed,
acquitted himself in that capacity with the
utmost readiness and address, changing the

courses as elegantly, and tasting everything first
as judiciously as any clerk of a kitchen. The
other sat and enjoyed himself like a delighted
epicure, tickled to the last degree with this new
turn of his affairs; when suddenly, a noise of
somebody opening the door, made them start
from their seats and scuttle in confusion about
the dining-room. Our country friend, in particular, was ready to die with fear at the barking
of a huge Mastiff or two, which opened their
throats just about the same time and made the
whole house echo. At last recovering himself,

"Well," says he, "if this be your town life,
much good may you do with it; give me my poor
quiet hole again, with my homely, but comfortable, grey peas."

IT IS BETTER TO ENJOY PLAIN FARE IN PEACE THAN THE
BEST OF LIVING IN FEAR.

THE FOX AND THE LION

THE first time the Fox saw the Lion he fell down at his feet, and was ready to die with fear. The second time he took courage, and could even bear to look upon him. The third time he had the impudence to come up to him, to salute him, and to enter into familiar conversation with him.

FAMILIARITY BREEDS CONTEMPT.

THE PEACOCK'S COMPLAINT

THE Peacock presented a memorial to Juno, importing how hardly he thought he was used in not having so good a voice as the Nightingale; how that pretty animal was agreeable to every ear that heard it, while he was laughed at for his ugly screaming noise if he did but open his mouth. The Goddess, concerned at the uneasiness of her favourite bird, answered him very kindly to this purpose:

"If the Nightingale is blest with a fine voice, you have the advantage in point of beauty and largeness of person."

"Ah," says he, "but what avails my silent, unmeaning beauty when I am so far excelled in voice ?"

The Goddess dismissed him, bidding him consider that the qualities of every creature were appointed by the decree of fate—to him beauty, strength to the Eagle, to the Nightingale a voice of melody, the faculty of speech to the Parrot, and to the Dove innocence. That each of these was contented with his own peculiar quality; and, unless he had a mind to be miserable, he must learn to be so too.

BE CONTENT WITH YOUR LOT.

THE PEACOCK AND THE MAGPIE

The Birds met together once upon a time to choose a king, and a Peacock, standing candidate, displayed his gaudy plumes and caught the eyes of the silly multitude with the richness of his feathers. The majority declared for him and clapped their wings with great applause. But just as they were going to proclaim him a Magpie stepped forth in the midst of the assembly, and addressed himself thus to the new king:

" May it please your Majesty elect, to permit one of your unworthy subjects to represent to you his suspicions and fears in the face of this whole congregation ; we have chosen you for our king, we have put our lives and fortunes into your hands, and our whole hope and dependence is upon you. If therefore the Eagle, or the Vulture, or the Kite should at any time make a descent upon us, as it is highly probable they will, may your Majesty be so gracious as to dispel our fears and clear our doubts about that matter, by letting us know how you intend to defend us against them ?"

HERCULES AND THE CARTER

This pithy, unanswerable question drew the whole audience into so just a reflection, that they soon resolved to proceed to a new choice. But from that time the Peacock has been looked upon as a vain insignificant pretender, and the Magpie esteemed as eminent a speaker as any in the whole community of birds.

BE LED BY WORTH RATHER THAN SHOW.

HERCULES AND THE CARTER

As a clownish fellow was driving his cart along a deep miry lane, the wheels stuck so fast in the clay that the horses could not draw them out. Upon this he fell a-bawling and praying to Hercules to come and help him. Hercules, looking down from a cloud, bid him not lie there like an idle rascal, but get up and whip his horses stoutly, and clap his shoulder to the wheel, adding that this was the only way for him to obtain his assistance

HELP COMES TO THOSE WHO HELP THEMSELVES.

THE PROUD FROG

AN OX, grazing in a meadow, chanced to set his foot among a parcel of young Frogs, and trod one of them to death. The rest informed their mother when she came home what had happened, telling her that the beast which did it was the hugest creature that they ever saw in their lives.

"What! was it so big?" says the old Frog, swelling and blowing up her speckled body to a great degree.

"Oh, bigger by a vast deal," say they.

"And so big?" says she, straining herself yet more.

"Indeed, mother," say they, "if you were to burst yourself you would never be so big."

She strove yet again, and burst herself indeed.

DO NOT TRY TO MAKE YOURSELF GREATER THAN YOU ARE.

The Proud Frog

"'What! was it so big?' says the old Frog, swelling and blowing up her speckled body to a great degree."

THE FIGHTING COCKS

Two Cocks were fighting for the sovereignty of the farmyard, and one of them having got the better of the other, he that was vanquished crept into a hole and hid himself for some time, but the victor flew to a conspicuous place, clapped his wings, and crowed out "Victory"! An Eagle who was watching for his prey near the place saw him, and, making a swoop, caught him in his talons and carried him off. The Cock that had been beaten seeing this, soon quitted his hole, and, shaking off all remembrance of his late disgrace, was very gallant with the hens from that time onwards.

DO NOT REJOICE OVER A FALLEN FOE.

THE ANT AND THE FLY

ONE day there happened some words between the Ant and the Fly about precedence, and the point was argued with great warmth and eagerness on both sides. Says the Fly :

"It is well known what my pretensions are, and how justly they are grounded ; there is never a sacrifice that is offered but I always taste of it, even before the gods themselves. I have one of the uppermost seats at church, and frequent the altar as often as anybody ; I have a free admission at court, and can never want the king's ear, for I sometimes sit upon his shoulders. There is not a maid-of-honour or handsome young creature comes in my way, but, if I like her, I settle betwixt her balmy lips. And then I eat and drink the best of everything without having any occasion to work for my living. What is there that such country creatures as you enjoy to be compared with a life like this ?"

The Ant, who by this time had composed herself, replied, with a great deal of self-control and no less severity :

THE ANT AND THE FLY

"Indeed, to be a guest at the entertainment of the gods is a very great honour if one is invited, but I should not care to be a disagreeable intruder anywhere. You talk of the king and the court, and the fine ladies there with great familiarity; but as I have been getting in my harvest in summer I have seen a certain person, under the town walls, making a hearty meal upon something that is not so proper to be mentioned. As to your frequenting the altars, you are in the right to take sanctuary where you are like to meet with the least disturbance; but I have known people before now run to altars and call it devotion when they have been shut out of all good company, and had nowhere else to go. You don't work for your living, you say—true; therefore when you have played away the summer and winter comes, you have nothing to live upon, and, while you are starving with cold and hunger, I have a good warm house over my head and plenty of provisions about me."

DON'T BOAST OF INTRUDING WHERE YOU ARE NOT WANTED.

THE WOLF AND THE CRANE

A WOLF, after devouring his prey, happened to have a bone stick in his throat, which gave him so much pain that he went howling up and down, and begging every creature he met to lend him a kind hand to relieve his sufferings; nay, he promised a reasonable reward to anyone that should undertake the operation with success. At last a Crane, tempted by the reward, and having first insisted that he should confirm his promise with an oath, undertook the business, and ventured his long neck into the rapacious fellow's throat. In short, he plucked out the bone, and expected the promised gratuity. When the Wolf, turning his eyes disdainfully towards him, said:

"I did not think you had been so unreasonable. I had your head in my mouth, and could have bit it off whenever I pleased, but suffered you to take it away without any damage, and yet you are not contented!"

IT IS NOT EASY FOR THE GREEDY TO BE GRATEFUL.

THE HORSE AND
THE LOADED ASS

An idle Horse and an Ass labouring under a heavy burden were travelling along a road together; they both belonged to a country fellow, who trudged it on foot by them. The Ass, ready to faint under his heavy load, entreated the Horse to assist him and lighten his burden by taking some of it upon his back. The Horse was ill-natured and refused to do it, upon which the poor Ass tumbled down in the middle of the highway, and expired in an instant. The countryman ungirded his pack-saddle and tried several ways to relieve him, but all to no purpose; so he took the whole burden and laid it upon the Horse, together with the skin of the dead Ass, so that the Horse, by his unkindness in refusing to do a small service, justly brought upon himself a great inconvenience.

THE LEOPARD AND THE FOX

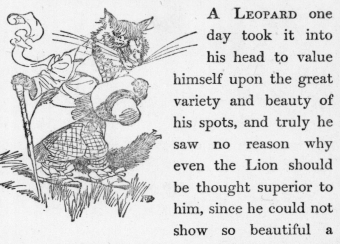

A LEOPARD one day took it into his head to value himself upon the great variety and beauty of his spots, and truly he saw no reason why even the Lion should be thought superior to him, since he could not show so beautiful a skin. As for the rest of the wild beasts of the forest, he treated them all, without distinction, in the most haughty and disdainful manner. But the Fox, being among them, went up to him with a great deal of spirit and resolution, and told him that he was mistaken in the value he was pleased to set upon himself; since people of judgement did not form their opinion of merit from an outside appearance, but by considering the good qualities and endowments with which the mind was stored within.

GREATNESS DOES NOT CONSIST IN OUTSIDE SHOW

THE BOY AND HIS MOTHER

A LITTLE Boy who went to school stole one of his schoolfellow's books, and brought it home to his Mother, who was so far from correcting and discouraging him on account of the theft, that she commended him and also gave him an apple for his pains. In process of time as the child grew up to be a man, he accustomed himself to greater robberies; and at last, being caught and committed to gaol, he was tried and condemned for felony. On the day of his execution as the officers were conducting him to the gallows, he was watched by a vast crowd of people, and among the rest by his Mother, who came sighing and sobbing along, and taking on extremely for her son's unhappy fate; which the criminal observing, called to the sheriff and begged a favour, that he would give him leave to speak a word or two to his poor, afflicted Mother. The sheriff, who would not deny a dying man so reasonable a request, gave him permission; and the felon, while, as everyone thought, he was whispering something of importance to his Mother, bit off her ear, to the great offence and surprise of the whole assembly !

"What," say they, "was not this villain contented with the evil deeds that he has already
committed, but that he must increase the number
of them by doing this violence to his Mother?"

"Good people," replied he, "I would not have
you be under a mistake; that wicked woman
deserves this and even worse at my hands, for if
she had chastised and reproved, instead of re-
warding and caressing me, when in my infancy I
stole a book from the school, I would not have
come to this ignominious and untimely end."

TRAIN UP A CHILD IN THE WAY HE SHOULD GO, AND WHEN
HE IS OLD HE WILL NOT DEPART THEREFROM.

THE WANTON CALF

A CALF, full of play and wantonness, seeing the
Ox at plough, could not help insulting him.
"What a sorry poor drudge art thou," says he,
"to bear that heavy yoke upon your neck, and
go all day drawing a plough at your tail, to turn
up the ground for your master! But you are a

wretched dull slave, and know no better, or else you would not do it. See what a happy life I lead; I go just where I please; sometimes I lie down in the cool shade; sometimes frisk about in the open sunshine; and, when I please, slake my thirst in the clear sweet brook: but you, if you were to perish, have not so much as a little dirty water to refresh you."

The Ox, not at all moved with what was said, went quietly and calmly on with his work; and in the evening was unyoked and turned loose. Soon after which he saw the Calf taken out of the field, and delivered into the hands of a priest, who immediately led him to the altar, and prepared to sacrifice him. His head was hung round with fillets of flowers, and the fatal knife was just going to be applied to his throat, when the Ox drew near and whispered to him:

"Behold the end of your insolence and arrogance; it was for this only you were suffered to live at all; and pray, now, friend, whose condition is best, yours or mine?"

DO NOT DESPISE HONEST LABOUR.

THE DEER AND THE LION

A DEER being hard pursued by the hounds found a cave, into which he rushed for security. But he was no sooner got in than he saw himself in the power of a Lion, who lay couched at the farther end of the cave, and sprung upon him in an instant. Being at the point of death, he complained thus:

"Unhappy creature that I am! I entered this cave to escape the pursuit of men and dogs, and am fallen into the jaws of the most cruel and rapacious of all wild beasts."

THE OLD MAN AND HIS SONS

AN old man had many Sons, who were often falling out with one another. When the father had exerted his authority, and used other means in order to reconcile them, and all to no purpose, at last he decided to do as follows :

He ordered his Sons to be called before him, and a short bundle of sticks to be brought, and then commanded them, one by one, to try if, with all their might and strength, they could any of them break it. They all tried, but to no purpose, for the sticks being closely and compactly bound up together, it was impossible for the force of man to do it. After this the father ordered the bundle to be untied, and gave a single stick to each of his Sons, at the same time bidding him try to break it, which, when each did with all imaginable ease, the father addressed himself to them to this effect.

"O my Sons, behold the power of unity ! For if you, in like manner, would but keep yourselves strictly joined together in the bonds of friendship, it would not be in the power of any mortal to hurt you ; but when once the ties of brotherly affection are dissolved, how soon do you fall to pieces, and are liable to be hurt by every injurious hand that assaults you !"

UNION IS STRENGTH.

THE PARROT AND HIS CAGE

A PARROT which belonged to a person of quality was fed every day with plenty of choice dainties, and kept in a stately Cage, which was placed upon a marble table in the garden, that he might enjoy the light of the sky and the freshness of the air to the best advantage. His master and all the family, when they talked to him, used the most tender, fond expressions, and the disorder of his feathers was smoothed with kindly touches by the fair hand of his lady. Yet notwithstanding this happy situation he was uneasy, and envied the condition of those birds who lived free in the wilderness, and hopped up and down, unconfined, from bough to bough. He earnestly longed to lead the same life, and secretly pined with grief because his wishes were denied him. After some time, however, it happened that the door of his cage was left unfastened, and the long-wished for opportunity was given him of making his escape. Accordingly, out he hopped and flew into the shades of a neighbouring wood, where he thought to spend the remainder of his days in content. But, alas! poor Poll was mistaken; a thousand inconveniences which he never dreamt of attended this elopement of his, and he is now really that miserable creature which before his imagination only made him. He is buffeted by the savage inhabitants of the grove, and his imitation of a human voice, which formerly rendered him so agreeable, does but the more expose him to the fierce resentment of the feathered nation. The delicate food with which he used to be fed is no more; he is unskilled in the ways of providing for himself, and even ready to die with hunger. A storm of rain, thunder, and lightning fills all the air, and he has no place to screen or protect him, his feathers are wetted with the heavy shower and scorched with the flashes of lightning. His tender nature, suited to a milder climate, could not stand the severe shock, he even died under it. But just before he breathed his last, he is said to have made this reflection:

"Ah, poor Poll, were you but in your own Cage again, you would never wander more."

EXPERIENCE IS A HARD SCHOOL.

THE FOX
WITHOUT A TAIL

A Fox, being caught in a steel trap by his tail, was glad to compound for his escape with the loss of it; but upon coming abroad into the world, began to be sensible of the disgrace such a defect would bring upon him, that he almost wished he had died rather than left it behind him. However, to make the best of a bad matter, he formed a project in his head to call an assembly of the rest of the Foxes, and propose it for their imitation, as a fashion which would be very agreeable and becoming. He did so, and made a long harangue upon the unprofitableness of tails in general, and endeavoured chiefly to show the awkwardness and inconvenience of a Fox's tail in particular, adding that it would be both more graceful and more expeditious to be altogether without them; and that, for his part, what he had only imagined and conjectured before, he now found by experience, because he never enjoyed himself so well nor found himself so easy as he had done since he cut off his tail. He said no more, but looked about with a brisk air to see what converts he had gained; when a sly old thief in the company, who understood traps, answered him with a grin:

"I believe you may have found it convenient to part with your tail, and when we are in the same circumstances, perhaps we may do so too."

DISTRUST INTERESTED ADVICE.

THE HARES AND THE FROGS

ONCE a great storm of wind blew among the trees and bushes, and made such a rustling among the leaves that the Hares—in a certain park, where there happened to be plenty of them— were so terribly frightened that they ran like mad all over the place, resolving to seek out some retreat of more security, or to end their unhappy days by doing violence to themselves. With this resolution they found an outlet where a pale had been broken down, and, bolting forth upon an adjoining common, had not run far before their course was stopped by a gentle brook, which glided across the way they intended to take. This was so grievous a disappointment that they were not able to bear it, and they determined rather to throw themselves headlong into the water, let what would become of it, than lead a life so full of dangers and crosses. But upon their coming to the brink of the river a parcel of Frogs, which were sitting there, frightened at their approach, leapt into the stream in great confusion, and dived to the very bottom for fear. Which a cunning old puss observing, called to the rest, and said:

"Hold, have a care what ye do. Here are other creatures, I perceive, which have their fears as well as us; don't, then, let us fancy ourselves the most miserable of any upon earth, but rather, by their example, learn to bear patiently those inconveniences which our nature has thrown upon us."

YOU ARE SELDOM SO BADLY OFF THAT THERE ARE NOT OTHERS IN A WORSE PLIGHT.

THE APE AND THE FOX

THE Ape meeting the Fox one day, humbly requested him to give him a piece of his fine, long, brush tail to cover his poor naked back, which was so exposed to all the violence and inclemency of the weather.

"For," says he, "Reynard, you have already more than you have occasion for, and a great part of it even drags along in the dirt."

The Fox answered:

"That as to his having too much, that was more than he knew; but be it as it would, he had rather sweep the ground with his tail as long as he lived than deprive himself of the least bit to cover the Ape's wretched back."

DO NOT ASK WHERE A REFUSAL MAY BE EXPECTED.

THE FIR-TREE AND THE BRAMBLE

A TALL, straight Fir-tree that stood towering up in the midst of a forest, was so proud of his dignity and high station, that he overlooked the little shrubs which grew beneath him. A Bramble, being one of the inferior throng, could by no means brook this haughty carriage, and therefore took him to task, and desired to know what he meant by it.

"Because," says the Fir-tree, "I look upon myself as the first tree for beauty and rank of any of the forest; my spring top shoots up into the clouds and my branches display themselves with perpetual beauty and greenness; while you lie grovelling upon the ground, liable to be crushed by every fool that comes near you, and impoverished by the luxurious droppings which fall from my leaves."

"All this may be true," replied the Bramble; "but when the woodman has marked you out for public use, and the sounding axe comes to be applied to your root, I am mistaken if you will not be glad to change conditions with the very worst of us."

GREATNESS DOES NOT MEAN SAFETY.

THE SPARROW AND
THE HARE

A HARE being seized by an Eagle squeaked out in a most woeful manner. A Sparrow that sat upon a tree just by and saw it, could not forbear being unseasonably witty, but called out, and said to the Hare:

"So ho! What, sit there and be killed! Prithee, up and away; I dare say, if you would but try, so swift a creature as you are would easily escape from the Eagle."

As he was going on with his cruel raillery down came a hawk and snapped him up, and, notwithstanding his vain cries and lamentations, began devouring him at once. The Hare, who was just expiring, yet received comfort from this accident even in the agonies of death, and, addressing her last words to the Sparrow, said:

"You, who just now insulted my misfortunes

with so much security, as you thought, may please to show us how well you can bear the like now it has befallen you."

DO NOT SCOFF AT ANOTHER'S ADVERSITY.

THE WOLF IN SHEEP'S CLOTHING

A WOLF clothing himself in the skin of a Sheep and getting in among the flock, by this means took the opportunity to devour many of them. At last the Shepherd discovered him, and cunningly fastened a rope about his neck, tying him up to a tree which stood hard by. Some other shepherds happening to pass that way and observing what he was about, drew near, and expressed their admiration at it.

"What," says one of them, "Brother, do you mean by hanging a Sheep?"

"No," replies the other, "but I hang a Wolf whenever I catch him, though in the habit and garb of a Sheep."

Then he showed them their mistake, and they applauded the justice of the execution.

OUTWARD APPEARANCES ARE DECEPTIVE.

ÆSOP AND THE IMPERTINENT
FELLOW

ÆSOP's master came home one day somewhat earlier than usual, and there happening to be no other slave in the house but Æsop, he was ordered to get supper ready as fast as he could. So away he ran to light a candle in order to kindle his fire, and the weather being warm and it wanting a good deal of night, he went up and down to several houses before he could find a light. At last, however, he found what he wanted, and, being in haste, he made no scruple of returning directly over the market-place, which was his nearest way home. But as he went along an impertinent fellow among the crowd caught him by the sleeve, and would fain have joked with him.

"O rare Æsop," says he, "what occasion for a candle, old boy? What, are you going to light the sun to bed?"

"Let me alone," says Æsop, "I am looking for a man."

HUMOUR CAN BE OUT OF PLACE.

THE SICK KITE

A KITE had been sick a long time, and, finding there was no hope of recovery, begged of his mother to go to all the churches and religious houses in the country to try what prayers and promises would effect on his behalf. The old Kite replied:

"Indeed, dear son, I would willingly undertake anything to save your life, but I have great reason to despair of doing you any service in the way you propose; for with what face can I ask anything of the gods in favour of one whose whole life has been a continual scene of rapine and injustice, and who has not scrupled, upon occasion, to rob the very altars themselves?"

REPENTANCE IS SOMETIMES TOO LATE.

142

THE VIPER AND THE FILE

A VIPER, entering a smith's shop, looked up and down for something to eat, and, seeing a File, fell to gnawing it as greedily as could be. The File told him very gruffly that he had best be quiet and let him alone, for he would get very little by nibbling at one who, upon occasion, could bite iron and steel.

IT IS USELESS TO ATTACK WHAT CANNOT BE INJURED.

THE HEN AND THE SWALLOW

A HEN finding some Serpent's eggs in a heap of old straw, sat upon them with a design to hatch them. A Swallow perceiving it, flew towards her with some warmth and passion:

"Are you mad," says she, "to sit hovering over a brood of such pernicious creatures as you do? Be assured the moment you bring them to light, you are the first they will attack and wreak their venomous spite upon."

DO NOT CAST PEARLS BEFORE SWINE.

THE SOW AND THE BITCH

A Sow and a Bitch happening to meet, a debate arose betwixt them concerning the size of their families. The Bitch insisted upon it that she had larger litters than any other four-legged creature.

"Ay," says the Sow, "you do indeed, but you are always in so much haste about it, that you bring your puppies into the world blind."

MORE HASTE LESS SPEED.

THE DOG IN THE MANGER

A Dog was lying upon a manger full of hay. An Ox being hungry, came near and offered to eat of the hay, but the envious, ill-natured cur, getting up and snarling at him, would not allow him to touch it. Upon which the Ox, in the bitterness of his heart, said :

"A curse light on thee for a malicious wretch, who wilt neither eat hay thyself, nor suffer others to do it."

DO NOT GRUDGE OTHERS WHAT YOU CANNOT ENJOY YOURSELF.

THE FOX AND THE SICK LION

IT was reported that the Lion was sick, and the beasts were made to believe that they could not show their respect better than by going to visit him. Upon this, nearly all the animals went; but it was particularly taken notice of, that the Fox was not one of the number. The Lion therefore despatched one of his Jackals to sound him about it, and ask him why he had so little charity and respect as never to come near him at a time when he lay so dangerously ill, and everybody else had been to see him.

"Why," replies the Fox, "pray, present my duty to his majesty, and tell him that I have the same respect for him as ever, and have been coming several times to kiss his royal hand, but I am so terribly frightened at the mouth of his cave, to see the print of my fellow subjects' feet, all pointing forwards, and none backwards, that I have not resolution enough to venture in."

Now, the truth of the matter was, that the sickness of the Lion was only a sham to draw the beasts into his den, the more easily to devour them.

THE ROAD TO RUIN IS EASIER GOING THAN RETURNING.

THE FOWLER AND THE RINGDOVE

A FOWLER took his gun and went into the woods to shoot. He spied a Ringdove among the branches of an oak, and intended to kill it. He clapped the piece to his shoulder and took his aim accordingly, but just as he was going to pull the trigger an adder, which he had trodden upon under the grass, bit him so painfully in the leg that he was forced to quit his design, and threw his gun down in a passion. The poison immediately infected his blood and his whole body began to mortify, which, when he perceived, he could not help owning to be just.

" Fate," says he, " has brought destruction upon me while I was contriving the death of another."

THE HARPER

A Fellow that used to play upon his Harp and sing to it in little alehouses, and made a shift by the help of those narrow, confined walls to please the dull drinkers who heard him, from hence entertained an ambition to show his skill in the public theatre, where he fancied he could not fail to raise a great reputation and fortune in a very short time. He was accordingly admitted upon trial, but the spaciousness of the place and the throng of the people so deadened and weakened both his voice and instrument, that scarcely either of them could be heard; and where they could it sounded so poor, so low, and wretched in the ears of his refined audience, that he was universally exploded and hissed off the stage.

BEWARE OF THE FLATTERY OF THE FOOLISH.

THE WOLF, THE FOX, AND THE APE

A WOLF indicted a Fox for a felony before an Ape, who upon that occasion was appointed special judge of the cause. The Fox gave in his answer to the Wolf's accusation, and denied the fact. So after a fair hearing on both sides, the Ape gave judgment to this purpose:

"I am of opinion that you," says he to the Wolf, "never lost the goods you sue for; and as for you" (turning to the Fox), "I make no question," said he, "but you have stolen what is laid to your charge, at least."

And thus the court was dismissed, with this public censure passed upon each party.

BEWARE OF LOSING YOUR GOOD NAME.

THE YOUNG MAN AND THE SWALLOW

A PRODIGAL young spendthrift, who had wasted his whole patrimony in taverns and gaming houses among fast, idle company, was taking a melancholy walk near a brook. It was in the month of January, and happened to be one of those warm sunshiny days which sometimes come even in that wintry season of the year; and to make it more flattering a Swallow, which had made his appearance by mistake too soon, flew skimming along upon the surface of the water. The giddy youth, observing this, without any further consideration concluded that summer was now come, and that he should have little or no occasion for clothes, so went and pawned them at the broker's, and ventured the money for one stake more among his sharping companions. When this, too, was gone the same way with the rest, he took another solitary walk in the same place as before. But the weather, being severe and frosty, had made everything look with an aspect very different from what it did before. The brook was quite frozen over, and the poor Swallow lay dead upon the bank of it, the very sight of which cooled the young spark's brains; and, coming to a sense of his misery, he reproached the dead bird as the author of all his misfortunes.

"Ah, wretch that thou wert!" says he; "thou hast undone both thyself and me, who was so credulous as to depend upon thee."

ONE SWALLOW DOES NOT MAKE A SUMMER.

THE BALD KNIGHT

A CERTAIN Knight growing old, his hair fell off, and he became bald; to hide which imperfection, he wore a periwig. But as he was riding out with some others a-hunting, a sudden gust of wind blew off the periwig, and exposed his bald pate. The company could not forbear laughing at the accident; and he himself laughed as loud as anybody, saying, "How was it to be expected that I should keep strange hair upon my head, when my own would not stay there?"

IF A JOKE IS MADE AGAINST YOU, ADD ANOTHER TO IT.

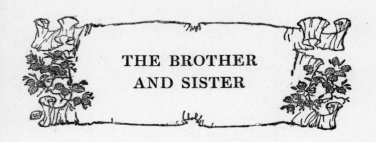

THE BROTHER
AND SISTER

A CERTAIN Man had two children, a Son and a
Daughter. The Boy, beautiful and handsome
enough; the Girl not quite so well favoured.
They were both very young, and happened one
day to be playing near the looking-glass which
stood on their mother's toilet table; the Boy,
pleased with the novelty of the thing, viewed
himself for some time, and in a wanton, roguish
manner pointed out to the Girl how handsome
he was. She resented it, and could not bear the
insolent manner in which he did it, for she understood it (as how could she do otherwise?) intended for a direct affront to her. Therefore she
ran immediately to her father, and with a great
deal of aggravation complained of her brother,
particularly for having acted so effeminate a part
as to look in a glass, and meddle with things
which belonged to women only. The father,

embracing them both with much tenderness and affection, told them that he should like to have them both look in the glass every day.

"To the intent that you," says he to the Boy, "if you think that face of yours handsome, may not disgrace and spoil it by an ugly temper and an improper behaviour."

"You," says he, speaking to the Girl, "that you may make up for the defects of your person, if there be any, by the sweetness of your manners and the agreeableness of your conversation."

THE TUNNY AND THE DOLPHIN

A FISH called a Tunny, being pursued by a Dolphin, and driven with great violence, not minding which way he went, was thrown by the force of the waves upon a rock, and left there. His death was now inevitable; but, casting his eyes on one side, and seeing the Dolphin in the same condition lie gasping by him:

"Well," says he, "I must die, it is true; but I die with pleasure, when I behold him who is the cause of it involved in the same fate."

THE FOX AND THE APE

'Reynard laughed heartily, and, going off, added with a sneer: 'You a King, and not understand a trap!''

THE FOX AND THE APE

ONCE upon a time the beasts were so void of reason as to choose an Ape for their king. He had danced and amused them with playing antic tricks, and truly nothing must serve but they must anoint him their sovereign. Accordingly crowned he was, and affected to look very wise and politic. But the Fox, vexed at his heart to see his fellow-brutes act so foolishly, was resolved at the first opportunity to convince them of their silly choice, and punish their jackanapes of a king for his presumption. Soon after, spying a trap in a ditch which was baited with a piece of flesh, he went and informed the Ape of it as a treasure which, being found upon the waste, belonged to his majesty only. The Ape, dreaming nothing of the matter, went very briskly to take possession, but he had no sooner laid his paws upon the bait than he was caught in the trap, where, betwixt shame and anger, he began to reproach the Fox, calling him rebel and traitor, and threatened to be revenged of him; at all which Reynard laughed heartily, and, going off, added with a sneer:

"You a king, and not understand a trap!"

THE FROGS
DESIRING A KING

THE Frogs, living an easy free life everywhere among the lakes and ponds, assembled together one day in a very tumultuous manner, and petitioned Jupiter to let them have a king who might inspect their morals and make them live a little honester. Jupiter, being at that time in pretty good-humour, was pleased to laugh heartily at their ridiculous request; and, throwing a little log down into the pool, cried: "There is a king for you." The sudden splash which this made by its fall into the water at first terrified them so exceedingly, that they were afraid to come near it. But in a little time, seeing it lie still without moving, they ventured by degrees to approach it; and at last, finding there was no danger, they leaped upon it, and, in short, treated it as familiarly as they pleased. But, not contented with so insipid a king as this was, they sent their deputies to petition again for another sort of one, for this they neither did nor could like. Upon that he sent them a Stork, who, without any ceremony, fell devouring and eating them up, one after another, as fast as he could. Then they applied themselves privately to Mercury, and got him to speak to Jupiter in their behalf, that he would be so good as to bless them again with another king, or restore them to their former state.

"No," says he, "since it was their own choice, let the obstinate wretches suffer the punishment due to their folly."

BE CONTENTED WITH YOUR CONDITION LEST A CHANGE BE FOR THE WORSE.

MERCURY AND THE WOODMAN

A MAN was felling a tree on the bank of a river, and by chance let his hatchet slip out of his hand, which dropped into the water and immediately sank to the bottom. Being therefore in great distress for the loss of his tool, he sat down and bemoaned himself most lamentably. Upon this Mercury appeared to him, and, being informed of the cause of his complaint, dived to the bottom of the river, and, coming up again, showed the Man a golden hatchet, demanding if that were his. He denied that it was. Upon which Mercury dived a second time, and brought up a silver one. The Man refused it, alleging likewise that this was not his. He dived a third time, and fetched up the actual hatchet the Man had lost; upon sight of which the poor wretch was overjoyed, and took it with all humility and thankfulness. Mercury was so pleased with the fellow's honesty that he gave him the other two into the bargain, as a reward for his just dealing. The Man went to his companions, and, giving them an account of what had happened, one of

THE KID AND THE WOLF

them went presently to the river's side, and let his hatchet fall designedly into the stream. Then, sitting down upon the bank, he fell a weeping and lamenting, as if he had been really and sorely afflicted. Mercury appeared as before, and, diving, brought him up a golden hatchet, asking if that was the hatchet he lost. Transported at the precious metal, he answered yes, and went to snatch at it greedily. But the god, detesting his abominable impudence, not only refused to give him that, but would not so much as let him have his own hatchet again.

HONESTY IS THE BEST POLICY.

THE KID AND THE WOLF

A KID being mounted upon the roof of a shed, and, seeing a Wolf below, loaded him with all manner of reproaches. Upon which the Wolf, looking up, replied:

"Do not value yourself, vain creature, upon thinking you mortify me, for I look upon this ill language as not coming from you, but from the place which protects you."

AT A SAFE DISTANCE IT IS EASY TO BE BRAVE.

THE FOX AND THE HEDGEHOG

A Fox was swimming across a river, and, when he came to the other side, he found the bank so steep and slippery that he could not get up it. But this was not all the misfortune, for while he stood in the water deliberating what to do, he was attacked by a swarm of flies, who, settling upon his head and eyes, stung and plagued him grievously. A Hedgehog, who stood upon the shore, beheld and pitied his condition, and offered to drive away the flies which molested and teased him in that manner.

"Friend," replies the Fox, "I thank you for your kind offer, but must desire you by no means to destroy these honest bloodsuckers that are now quartered upon me, and who are, I fancy,

153

pretty well filled, for if they should leave me a
fresh swarm would take their places, and I should
not have a drop of blood left in my whole body."

THE OAK AND THE REED

AN Oak, which hung over the bank of a river,
was blown down by a violent storm of wind;
and as it was carried along by the stream, some
of its boughs brushed against a reed which grew
near the shore. This struck the Oak with a
thought of admiration; and he could not forbear
asking the Reed how he came to stand so secure
and unhurt in a tempest which had been furious
enough to tear an Oak up by the roots.

"Why," says the Reed, "I secure myself by
putting on a behaviour quite contrary to what
you do: instead of being stubborn and stiff, and
confiding in my strength, I yield and bend to
the blast, and let it go over me, knowing how
vain and fruitless it would be to resist."

BETTER BEND THAN BREAK.

THE ASS AND THE LITTLE DOG

THE Ass, observing how great a favourite the
little Dog was with his master, how much
caressed and fondled and fed with good bits at
every meal, and for no other reason, as far as
he could see, but skipping and frisking about,
wagging his tail, and leaping up in his master's
lap ; he was resolved to imitate the same, and see
whether such a behaviour would not procure him
the same favours. Accordingly, the master had
no sooner come home from walking about his
fields and gardens, and was seated in his easy-
chair, but the Ass, who observed him, came
gambolling and braying towards him in a very
awkward manner. The master could not help
laughing aloud at the odd sight. But his jest
was soon turned into earnest when he felt the
rough salute of the Ass's fore-feet, who, raising
himself upon his hind legs, pawed against his
breast with a most loving air, and would fain
have jumped into his lap. The good man, terrified
at this outrageous behaviour, and unable to
endure the weight of so heavy a beast, cried out;
upon which one of his servants, running in with

The Ass and the Little Dog

"The Ass, raising himself upon his hind legs, pawed against his breast with a most loving air, and would fain have jumped into his lap."

a good stick, and laying heartily upon the bones of the poor Ass, soon convinced him that everyone who desires it is not qualified to be a favourite.

IT IS WISER FOR THE SLOW-WITTED NOT TO JOKE.

THE WOOD AND THE CLOWN

A COUNTRY fellow came one day into a wood and looked about him with some concern, upon which the Trees, with a curiosity natural to some other creatures, asked him what he wanted. He replied that he only wanted a piece of wood to make a handle to his hatchet. Since that was all, it was voted unanimously that he should have a piece of good, sound, tough ash. But he had no sooner received and fitted it for his purpose than he began to lay about him unmercifully, and to hack and hew without distinction, felling the noblest trees in all the forest. The Oak is said to have spoken thus to the Beech in a low whisper :

" Brother, we must take it for our pains."

FOOLISH FOLK GIVE HELP TO THE ENEMY.

THE WOLVES AND THE SICK ASS

An Ass being sick, the report of it was spread abroad in the country, and some did not hesitate to say, that she would die before another night passed over her head. Upon this several Wolves came to the stable where she lay, under pretence of making her a visit; but, rapping at the door and asking how she did, the young Ass came out, and told them that his mother was much better than they desired.

THE BEES, THE DRONES, AND THE WASP

A parcel of Drones got into a hive among the Bees and disputed the ownership with them, swearing that the honey and the combs were their goods. The Bees were obliged to go to law with them, and a Wasp happened to be judge of the cause, one who was well acquainted with the nature of each, and therefore the better qualified to decide the controversy between them. Accordingly:

"Gentlemen," says he, speaking to both plaintiff and defendant, "the usual method of proceeding in these courts is pretty expensive and slow withal; therefore, as you are both my friends and I wish you well, I desire you would refer the matter to me, and I will decide betwixt you instantly."

They were both pleased with the offer, and returned him thanks.

"Why, then," says he, "that it may appear who are the just proprietors of these honeycombs (for being both so nearly alike as you are in colour, I must needs own the point is somewhat dubious, do you)," addressing himself to the Bees, "take one hive; you," speaking to the Drones, "another; and go to making honey as fast as you can, that we may know by the taste and colour of it who has the best title to this in dispute."

The Bees readily accepted the proposal, but the Drones would not stand to it. And so Judge Wasp, without any further ceremony, declared in favour of the former.

THE MULE

A MULE, which was well fed and worked little, grew fat and wanton, and frisked about very notably.

" And why should not I run as well as the best of them ?" says he. " It is well known I had a horse for my father, and a very good racer he was."

Soon after this his master took him out, and being upon urgent business, whipped and spurred the Mule to make him go faster, who, beginning to tire upon the road, changed his note, and said to himself:

" Ah, where is the horse's blood you boasted of but now ? I am sorry to say it, friend, but indeed your worthy father was an Ass, and not a Horse."

DO NOT BLAME YOUR PARENTS FOR YOUR OWN SHORTCOMINGS.

THE HAWK AND
THE NIGHTINGALE

A NIGHTINGALE, sitting
all alone among the shady
branches of an oak, sung
with so melodious and shrill a pipe that she
made the woods echo again, and alarmed a
hungry Hawk, who was at some distance off,
watching for his prey. He had no sooner discovered the little musician, but, making a swoop
at the place, he seized her with his crooked
talons and bid her prepare for death.

"Ah," says she, "for mercy's sake don't do so
barbarous a thing, and so unbecoming to yourself;
consider I never did you any wrong, and am but
a poor small morsel for such a stomach as yours;
rather attack some larger fowl, which may bring
you more credit and a better meal, and let
me go."

"Ay," says the Hawk, "persuade me to it if

you can. I have been upon the watch all the day long, and have not met with one bit of anything till I caught you; and now you would have me let you go, in hopes of something better, would you? Pray, who would be the fool then?"

A BIRD IN THE HAND IS WORTH TWO IN THE BUSH.

THE YOUNG MAN AND HIS CAT

JUPITER was once discussing with Venus whether it was possible for any living creature to change its nature. Venus thought it impossible, but Jupiter thought otherwise, and, wishing to test the question, turned a cat into a young and charming woman, and a man falling in love with her, she soon afterwards became his wife. Jupiter pointed out to Venus how well she behaved at the wedding-feast and urged that her nature had surely changed. At night, however, Venus let loose a mouse in the room, which the bride no sooner spied than she jumped up and pounced on it. Venus therefore changed her back to a cat once more.

NATURE WILL OUT.

THE FOX AND THE BOAR

A Boar stood whetting his tusks against an old tree. A Fox, who happened to come by at the same time, asked him why he made those martial preparations of whetting his teeth, since there was no enemy near that he could perceive.

"That may be, Master Reynard," says the Boar; "but we should sharpen our arms while we have leisure, you know, for in time of danger we shall have something else to do."

THE DOG AND THE SHEEP

A Dog sued a Sheep for a debt, of which a Kite and a Wolf were to be judges; they, without debating long upon the matter or making any scruple for want of evidence, gave sentence for the plaintiff, who immediately tore the poor Sheep in pieces and divided the spoil with the unjust judges.

THE DOG AND THE WOLF

A LEAN, hungry, half-starved Wolf happened one moonlight night to meet with a jolly, plump, well-fed Mastiff; and, after the first compliments were passed, says the Wolf:

"You look extremely well. I protest I think I never saw a more graceful, comely person; but how comes it about, I beseech you, that you should live so much better than I? I may say without vanity that I venture fifty times more than you do, and yet I am almost ready to perish with hunger."

The Dog answered very bluntly:

"Why, you may live as well if you will do the same for it that I do."

"Indeed! What is that?" says he.

"Why," says the Dog, "only to guard the house a-nights and keep it from thieves."

"With all my heart," replies the Wolf, "for at present I have but a sorry time of it; and I think to change my hard lodging in the woods, where I endure rain, frost, and snow, for a warm roof over my head and plenty of good victuals, will be no bad bargain."

THE DOG AND THE WOLF

"True," says the Dog; "therefore you have nothing more to do than to follow me."

Now, as they were jogging on together the Wolf spied a crease in the Dog's neck, and, having a strange curiosity, could not forbear asking him what it meant.

"Pugh! Nothing," says the Dog.

"Nay, but pray," says the Wolf.

"Why," says the Dog, "if you must know, I am tied up in the daytime because I am a little fierce, for fear I should bite people, and am only let loose a-nights. But this is done with a design to make me sleep a-days, more than anything else, and that I may watch the better in the night-time; for as soon as ever the twilight appears out I am turned, and may go where I please. Then my master brings me plates of bones from the table with his own hands, and whatever scraps are left by any of the family all fall to my share, for you must know I am a favourite with everybody. So you see how you are to live. Come, come along. What is the matter with you?"

"No," replied the Wolf, "I beg your pardon;

keep your happiness all to yourself. Liberty is the word with me, and I would not be a king upon the terms you mention."

RATHER GO HUNGRY IN FREEDOM THAN FEED WELL IN
SLAVERY.

THE ONE-EYED DOE

A Doe that had but one eye used to graze near the sea, and that she might be the more secure from harm she kept her blind side towards the water, from whence she had no fear of danger, and with the other surveyed the country as she fed. By this vigilance and precaution she thought herself in the utmost security, when a sly fellow, with two or three of his companions, who had been poaching after her several days to no purpose, at last took a boat, and going some way round upon the sea, came gently down upon her and shot her. The Doe, in the agonies of death, breathed out this doleful complaint:

" O hard fate! that I should receive my death's wound from that side whence I expected no ill, and be safe in that part where I looked for the most danger."

THE YOUNG MEN AND THE COOK

Two young Men went into a Cook's shop under pretence of buying meat, and while the Cook's back was turned one of them snatched up a piece of beef and gave it to his companion, who presently clapped it under his cloak. The Cook, turning about again and missing his beef, began to charge them with it, upon which he that first took it swore fiercely he had none of it. He that had it swore as heartily that he had taken up none of his meat.

"Why, look ye, gentlemen," says the Cook, "I see your equivocation; and though I cannot tell which of you has taken my meat, I am sure between you both there is a thief and a couple of rascals."

A BAD DEED IS NO BETTER FOR BEING SHARED.

THE THIEF AND THE DOG

A THIEF coming to rob a certain house in the night was disturbed in his attempts by a fierce, vigilant Dog, who kept barking at him continually. Upon which the Thief, thinking to stop his mouth, threw him a piece of bread, but the Dog refused it with indignation, telling him that before he only suspected him to be a bad man; but now, upon his offering to bribe him, he was confirmed in his opinion, and that as he was intrusted with the guardianship of his master's house, he should never cease barking while such a rogue as he lay lurking about it.

THE SHEEP-BITER

A CERTAIN Shepherd had a Dog upon whose fidelity he relied very much, for whenever he had an occasion to be absent himself, he committed the care and tuition of the flock to the charge of his Dog; and, to encourage him to do his duty cheerfully, he fed him constantly with sweet curds and whey, and sometimes threw him a crust or two in addition. Yet, notwithstanding this, no sooner was his back turned but the treacherous cur fell foul upon the flock, and devoured the sheep instead of guarding and defending them. The Shepherd, being informed of this, was resolved to hang him; and the Dog, when the rope was about his neck and he was just going to be tied up, began to expostulate with his master, asking him why he was so unmercifully bent against him, who was his own servant and creature, and had only committed one or two crimes; and why he did not rather execute revenge upon the Wolf, who was a constant and declared enemy.

"Nay," replies the Shepherd, "it is for that very reason that I think you ten times more worthy of death than he; from him I expected nothing but hostilities, and therefore could guard against him. You I depended upon as a just and faithful servant, and fed and encouraged you accordingly, and therefore your treachery is the more notorious, and your ingratitude the more unpardonable."

A TREACHEROUS FRIEND IS WORSE THAN AN OPEN ENEMY.

JUPITER AND PALLAS

ONCE upon a time the Heathen gods had a mind to adopt each a particular tree into their patronage and tuition. Jupiter chose the Oak, Venus was pleased to name the Myrtle, Apollo pitched upon the Laurel, Cybele took the Pine, and Hercules the Poplar. Pallas, being present, expressed her admiration at their fancy in making choice of trees that bore nothing.

"Oh," says Jupiter, "the reason of that is plain enough, for we would not be thought to dispense our favours with any mercenary view."

"You may do as you please," says she, "but let the Olive be my tree; and I declare my reason for choosing it is, because it bears plenty of noble useful fruit."

Upon which the Thunderer, putting on a serious composed gravity, spoke thus to the Goddess:

THE BEAR AND THE BEE-HIVES

" Indeed, daughter, it is not without justice that you are so celebrated for your wisdom, for unless some benefit attend your actions, to perform them only for the sake of glory, is but a silly business."

EMPTY GLORY IS A VAIN PURSUIT.

THE BEAR AND THE BEE-HIVES

A BEAR, climbing over the fence into a place where the Bees were kept, began to plunder the Hives and rob them of their honey. But the Bees, to revenge the injury, attacked him in a whole swarm together ; and though they were not able to pierce his rugged hide, yet with their little stings they so annoyed his eyes and nostrils, that, unable to endure the smarting pain, with impatience he tore the skin over his ears with his own claws, and suffered ample punishment for the injury he did the Bees in breaking open their waxen cells.

SOME DESIRES ARE SATISFIED AT TOO GREAT A PRICE.

THE RIVER-FISH AND THE SEA-FISH

THE waters of a river being mightily swelled by a great flood, the stream ran down with a violent current, and by its rapid force carried a huge Barbel along with it into the sea. This fresh-water spark had no sooner come into a new climate but he began to give himself airs, to talk big, and look with contempt upon the inhabitants of the place. He boasted that he was of a better country and family than any among them, for which reason they ought to give place to him, and pay him respect accordingly. A fine large Mullet, that happened to swim near him and heard his insolent language, bid him hold his silly tongue, for if they should be taken by fishermen and carried to market, he would soon be convinced who ought to have the preference.

" We," says he, " should be bought up at any price for tables of the first quality, and you sold to the poor for little or nothing."

IT IS GOOD TO KNOW YOUR MARKET VALUE.

A BOAR CHALLENGES AN ASS

A BOAR and an Ass having fallen out, the Boar
challenged the Ass to fight. Having his power-
ful tusks to depend upon, the Boar could not
help comparing the comparatively harmless head
of the Ass to his own, and felt quite confident
of success. At length the appointed time for
the fight arrived, and the two combatants
approached one another, the Boar rushing
suddenly upon his opponent; but the Ass
quickly turned aside, and kicked out with his
hoofs as hard as he could: catching the Boar
full in the jaws, he was rolled over in the dust.

"Well," he said, "how could I expect an
attack from that end?"

DANGER COMES FROM MORE THAN ONE SOURCE.

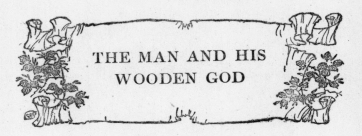

THE MAN AND HIS WOODEN GOD

A MAN having a Wooden God worshipped it every day, and, among other things, prayed particularly for wealth because his circumstances were but low. But when he had continued to do this for many days to no purpose, in a passion at the disappointment he took the image by the legs, knocked it against the pavement, and broke it in pieces, upon which a great quantity of money, which had been enclosed within it, flew about the room. The man no sooner perceived this, but, addressing himself to the idol:

"Thou obstinate, perverse deity," says he, "who, while I humbly besought thee hadst no regard to my prayers, but now thou art used ill and broken to pieces, dost pour forth good things in even a greater abundance than I could desire."

178

THE COLLIER AND THE FULLER

THE Collier and the Fuller, being old acquaintances, happened once upon a time to meet together; and the latter, being ill provided with a habitation, was invited by the former to come and live in the same house with him.

"I thank you, my dear friend," replied the Fuller, "for your kind offer, but it cannot be; for if I were to dwell with you, whatever I should take pains to scour and make clean in the morning, the dust of you and your coals would blacken and defile as bad as ever before night."

CLEANLINESS AND DIRT CANNOT BE FRIENDS.

THE HUSBANDMAN AND THE STORK

THE Husbandman pitched a net in his fields to take the Cranes and Geese which came to feed upon the newly-sown corn. Accordingly he took several, both Cranes and Geese, and among them a Stork who had pleaded hard for his life, and among other apologies which he made, he said:

"That he was neither Goose nor Crane, but a

179

poor, harmless Stork, who performed his duty to his parents to all intents and purposes, feeding them when they were old, and, as occasion required, carrying them from place to place upon his back."

"All this may be true," replies the Husbandman; "but as I have taken you in bad company and in the same crime, you must expect to suffer the same punishment."

WE ARE JUDGED BY THE COMPANY WE KEEP.

ÆSOP AT PLAY

AN Athenian one day found Æsop at play with a company of little boys at their childish diversions, and began to jeer and laugh at him for it. The old fellow, who was too much a wag himself to suffer others to ridicule him, took a bow, unstrung, and laid it upon the ground. Then, calling the censorious Athenian.

"Now, philosopher," says he, "expound the riddle if you can, and tell us what the unstrained bow implies."

The Man, after racking his brains and scratching his pate about it a considerable time to no purpose, at last gave it up, and declared he knew not what to make of it.

"Why," says Æsop, laughing, "if you keep a bow always bent, it will break presently; but if you let it go slack, it will be the fitter for use when you want it."

ALL WORK AND NO PLAY MAKES JACK A DULL BOY.

THE HUNTED BEAVER

IT is said that a Beaver (a creature that lives chiefly in the water) has a certain part about him which is good in physic, and that, upon this account, he is often hunted down and killed. Once upon a time, as one of these creatures was hard pursued by the Dogs, and knew not how to escape, recollecting within himself the reason of his being thus persecuted, with a great resolution and presence of mind he bit off the part which his hunters wanted, and, throwing it towards them, by these means escaped with his life.

IT IS BETTER TO GIVE A PART THAN TO LOSE ALL

THE JACKDAW AND THE SHEEP

A JACKDAW sat chattering upon the back of a Sheep.

"Peace, you noisy thing," says the Sheep; "if I were a dog, you durst not serve me so."

"That is true enough," replies the Jackdaw, "I know very well who I have to do with. I never meddle with the surly and revengeful; but I love to plague such poor, helpless creatures as you are, that cannot do me any harm again."

THE OLD HOUND

AN old Hound, who had been an excellent good one in his time, and given his master great sport and satisfaction in many a chase, at last, by the effect of years, became feeble and unserviceable. However, being in the field one day when the Stag was almost run down, he happened to be the first that came in with him, and seized him by one of his haunches; but his decayed and broken teeth not being able to keep their hold, the Deer escaped, and threw him quite out. Upon which his master, being in a great passion, and going to strike him, the honest old creature is said to have barked out this apology:

"Ah, do not strike your poor old servant; it is not my heart and inclination, but my strength and speed that fail me. If what I now am displeases, pray don't forget what I have been."

THE TRUMPETER TAKEN PRISONER

A TRUMPETER being taken prisoner in a battle begged hard for quarter, declaring his innocence and protesting that he neither had, nor could kill any man, bearing no arms, but only a trumpet, which he was obliged to sound at the word of command.

"For that reason," replied his enemies, "we are determined not to spare you; for, though you yourself never fight, yet with that wicked instrument of yours you blow up animosity between other people, and so become the occasion of much bloodshed."

THE CREAKING WHEEL

THE Coachman, hearing one of the wheels of his coach creak, was surprised, but more especially when he perceived that it was the worst Wheel of the whole set, and which he thought had but little pretence to take such a liberty. But upon his demanding the reason why it did so, the Wheel replied, that it was natural for people who laboured under any affliction or infirmity to complain.

THE FALCONER AND THE PARTRIDGE

A FALCONER having taken a Partridge in his nets the bird begged hard for a reprieve, and promised the man, if he would let him go, to decoy other Partridges into his net.

"No," replies the Falconer, "I was before determined not to spare you, but now you have condemned yourself by your own words, for he who is such a scoundrel as to offer to betray his friends to save himself, deserves, if possible, worse than death."

THE TRAITOR HAS NO FRIENDS.

THE FOX IN THE WELL

A Fox having fallen into a well, made a shift, by sticking his claws into the sides, to keep his head above water. Soon after a Wolf came and peeped over the brink, to whom the Fox applied himself very earnestly for assistance; entreating that he would help him with a rope, or something of that kind, which might assist him to escape. The Wolf, moved with compassion at his misfortune, could not forbear expressing his concern:

"Ah, poor Reynard," says he, "I am sorry for you with all my heart. How could you possibly come into this melancholy condition?"

"Nay; prithee, friend," replies the Fox, "if you wish me well do not stand pitying me. but

lend me some succour as fast as you can, for pity
is but cold comfort when one is up to the chin in
water, and within a hair's-breadth of starving or
drowning."

PITY IS POOR COMFORT.

THE HART AND THE VINE

A Hart being pursued hard by the hunters, hid
himself under the broad leaves of a shady spreading Vine. When the hunters were gone by and
had given him over for lost, he, thinking himself
very secure, began to crop and eat the leaves of
the Vine. By this means the branches being put
into a rustling motion, drew the eyes of the
hunters that way ; who, seeing the Vine stir and
fancying some wild beast had taken covert there,
shot their arrows at a venture and killed the
Hart, who, before he expired, uttered his dying
words to this purpose :

"Ah, 1 suffer justly for my ingratitude, who
could not forbear doing an injury to the Vine,
that so kindly concealed me in time of danger."

THE NURSE AND THE WOLF

A Nurse, who was endeavouring to quiet a tiresome bawling child, among other attempts, threatened to throw it out of doors to the Wolf, if it did not leave off crying. A Wolf, who chanced to be prowling near the door just at that time, heard the expression, and, believing the woman to be in earnest, waited a long while about the house in expectation of seeing her words made good. But at last the child, wearied with its own importunities, fell asleep, and the poor Wolf was forced to return back to the woods empty and supperless.

The Fox meeting him, and surprised to see him going home so thin and disconsolate, asked him what the matter was, and how he came to fare no better that night.

" Ah ! do not ask me," says he ; " I was so silly as to believe what the Nurse said, and have been disappointed."

THE STAG IN THE OX-STALL

A STAG, roused out of his thick covert in the midst of the forest, and driven hard by the hounds, made towards a farmhouse, and seeing the door of an ox-stall open, entered therein, and hid himself under a heap of straw. One of the Oxen, turning his head about, asked him what he meant by venturing himself in such a place as that was, where he was sure to meet with his doom!

" Ah," says the Stag, " if you will but be so good as to favour me with your concealment, I hope I shall do well enough ; I intend to make off again at the first opportunity."

Well, he stayed there till towards night, when in came the ox man with a bundle of fodder, and never saw him. In short, all the servants of the farm came and went, and not a soul of them suspected anything of the matter. Nay, the bailiff himself came, according to form, and looked in, but walked away, no wiser than the rest. Upon this the Stag, ready to jump out of his skin for joy, began to return thanks to the good-natured Oxen, protesting that they were the most obliging people he had ever met with in his life. After he had done his compliments, one of them answered him gravely:

"Indeed, we desire nothing more than to have it in our power to contribute to your escape, but there is a certain person you little think of who has a hundred eyes; if he should happen to come, I would not give this straw for your life."

In the meantime home comes the master himself from a neighbour's, where he had been invited to dinner; and, because he had observed the cattle to look but scurvily of late, he went up to the rack, and asked why they did not give them more fodder; then, casting his eyes downward:

"Hey-day," says he, "why so sparing of your litter? Pray scatter a little more here. And these cobwebs—but I have spoken so often that unless I do it myself——"

Thus, as he went on prying into everything, he chanced to look where the Stag's horns lay sticking out of the straw; upon which he raised a hue and cry, called all his people about him, killed the poor Stag, and made a prize of him.

THE MASTER'S EYE SEES MOST.

THE MOLE AND HER MOTHER

A YOUNG Mole snuffed up her nose, and told her Mother she smelt an odd kind of a smell. By-and-by:

"Oh, strange," says she, "what a noise there is in my ears, as if ten thousand mills were going."

A little after she was at it again:

"Look, look! What is that I see yonder? It is just like the flame of a fiery furnace."

To whom the Mother replied:

"Prithee, child, hold your idle tongue; and if you would have us allow you any sense at all, do not effect to show more than nature has given you."

DO NOT TRY TO BE THOUGHT MORE CLEVER THAN YOU ARE.

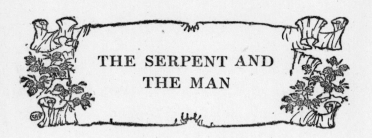

THE SERPENT AND THE MAN

A CHILD was playing in a meadow, and by chance trod upon a Serpent. The Serpent, in the fury of his passion, turned up and bit the child with his poisonous teeth, so that he died immediately. The father of the child, inspired with grief and revenge, took a weapon in his hand, and, pursuing the Serpent, before he could get into his hole struck at him and lopped off a piece of his tail. The next day, hoping by stratagem to finish his revenge, he brought to the Serpent's hole honey, meal, and salt, and desired him to come forth, protesting that he only sought a reconciliation on both sides. However, he was not able to decoy the Serpent forth, who only hissed from within to this purpose:

"In vain you attempt a reconciliation, for as long as the memory of the dead child and the mangled tail subsists, it will be impossible for you and me to have any charity for each other."

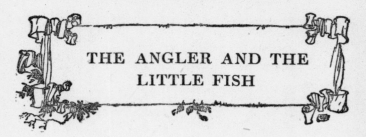

THE ANGLER AND THE LITTLE FISH

A MAN was angling in a river, and caught a small Perch, which, as he was taking off the hook, and going to put it into his basket, opened his mouth and began to implore his pity, begging that he would throw it into the river again. Upon the Man's demanding what reason he had to expect such a favour:

"Why," says the Fish, "because at present I am but young and little, and consequently not so well worth your while as I shall be if you take me some time hence, when I am grown larger."

"That may be," replies the Man, "but I am not one of those fools who quit a certainty in expectation of an uncertainty."

USE YOUR OPPORTUNITY WHEN IT COMES.

THE SATYR AND THE TRAVELLER

A SATYR, as he was ranging the forest in an exceedingly cold snowy season, met with a Traveller half-starved with the extremity of the weather. He took compassion on him, and kindly invited him to a warm comfortable home he had in the hollow of a tree. As soon as they had entered and sat down, the chill Traveller could not forbear blowing his fingers' ends. Upon the Satyr's asking him why he did so, he answered that he did it to warm his hands. The honest Sylvan, having seen little of the world, admired a man who was master of so valuable a quality as that of blowing heat, and therefore was resolved to entertain him in the best manner he could. He produced a dish of smoking porridge and presented to his shivering guest. But this the Traveller thought fit to blow likewise; and upon the Satyr's demanding a reason why he blowed again, he replied, to cool his dish. This second answer provoked the Satyr's indignation as much as the first had kindled his surprise; so taking the Man by the shoulder, he thrust him out of doors, saying he would have nothing to do with a wretch who had so vile a quality as to blow hot and cold with the same mouth.

DO NOT ACT HARSHLY IN A HURRY.

JUPITER AND THE HERDSMAN

A HERDSMAN, missing a young heifer that belonged to his herd, went up and down the forest to seek it. And having walked a great deal of ground to no purpose, he fell a praying to Jupiter for relief, promising to sacrifice a kid to him if he would help him to a discovery of the thief. After this he went on a little farther, and came near a grove of oaks, where he found the carcass of his heifer, and a lion grumbling over it and feeding upon it. The sight almost scared him out of his wits, so down he fell upon his knees once more, and, addressing himself to Jupiter:

"O Jupiter," says he, "I promised thee a kid to show me the thief, but now I promise thee a bull if thou wilt be so merciful as to deliver me out of his clutches."

THE BOASTING TRAVELLER

ONE who had been abroad, at his return home
again was giving an account of his travels; and,
among other places, said he had been at Rhodes,
where he had so distinguished himself in leaping,
an exercise that city was famous for, that no
Rhodian could come near him. When those
who were present did not seem to credit this
relation so readily as he intended they should, he
took some pains to convince them of it by oaths
and protestations; upon which one of the company, rising up, told him he need not give himself so much trouble about it, since he would put
him in a way to demonstrate it in fact, which
was to suppose the place they were in to be
Rhodes, and to perform his extraordinary leap
over again. The Boaster, not liking this proposal, sat down quietly, and had no more to say
for himself.

THE EAGLE AND THE CROW

An Eagle flew down from the top of a high rock and settled upon the back of a lamb, and then instantly flying up into the air again, bore his bleating prize aloft in his talons. A Crow who sat upon an elm and beheld his exploit, resolved to imitate it, so flying down upon the back of a Ram and entangling his claws in the wool, he fell a-chattering and attempted to fly, by which means he drew the observation of the shepherd upon him, who, finding his feet hampered in the fleece of the Ram, easily took him, and gave him to his boys for their sport and diversion.

IT IS DANGEROUS TO OVERESTIMATE YOUR OWN CAPACITY.

THE PLOUGHMAN AND FORTUNE

A Ploughman as he was ploughing the ground found a treasure. Transported with joy, he immediately began to return thanks to the ground, which had been so liberal and kind to him. Fortune observed what he did, and could not forbear showing her resentment of it. She instantly appeared to him, and :

THE PORCUPINE AND THE SNAKES

"You fool," says she, "what a blockhead are you to lie thanking the ground thus and take no notice of me. You woodenhead, if you had lost such a treasure instead of finding it, I should have been the first you would have laid the blame upon."

GIVE YOUR THANKS WHERE THEY ARE DUE.

THE PORCUPINE AND THE SNAKES

A PORCUPINE, wanting to shelter himself, desired a nest of Snakes to give him admittance into their cave. They were prevailed upon, and let him in accordingly, but were so annoyed with his sharp, prickly quills that they soon repented of their easy compliance, and entreated the Porcupine to withdraw and leave them their hole to themselves.

"No," says he, "let them quit the place that don't like it; for my part, I am well enough satisfied as I am."

YOU CANNOT CHOOSE YOUR PARTNER TOO CAREFULLY.

THE COUNTRYMAN AND THE SNAKE

A Villager, in a frosty, snowy winter, found a Snake under a hedge almost dead with cold. He could not help having compassion for the poor creature, so brought it home and laid it upon the hearth near the fire, but it had not lain there long before—being revived with the heat— it began to erect itself and fly at his wife and children, filling the whole cottage with dreadful hissings. The Countryman, hearing an outcry, and perceiving what the matter was, caught up a spade and soon despatched him, upbraiding him at the same time in these words:

"Is this, vile wretch, the reward you make to him that saved your life? Die, as you deserve, but a single death is too good for you."

THE UNGRATEFUL RETURN EVIL FOR GOOD.

THE TRAVELLERS

Two men travelling upon the road, one of them saw an axe lying upon the ground, where somebody had been hewing timber, so, taking it up, says he :

" I have found an axe."

" Do not say *I*," says the other, "but *we* have found, for as we are companions, we ought to share it betwixt us."

But the first would not consent. However, they had not gone far before the owner of the axe, hearing what was become of it, pursued them with a warrant, which, when the fellow that had it, perceived :

" Alas !" says he to his companion, " we are undone."

" Nay," says the other, " do not say *we*, but *I* am undone, for as you would not let me share the prize, neither will I share the danger with you."

OWNERSHIP ENTAILS RESPONSIBILITY.

THE OWL AND THE GRASSHOPPER

AN OWL sat sleeping in a tree, but a Grass-hopper, who was playing on a fiddle beneath, would not let her be quiet, abusing her with very indecent and uncivil language ; telling her she was a scandalous person, who plied a-nights to get a living and shut herself up all day in a hollow tree. The Owl desired her to hold her tongue and be quiet, notwithstanding which she was the more impertinent. She begged of her a second time to leave off, but all to no purpose. The Owl, vexed at the heart to find that all she said went for nothing, cast about to coax her by stratagem.

"Well," says she, "since one must be kept awake it is a pleasure, however, to be kept awake by such pleasant music, which, I must confess, is no ways inferior to the finest harp. And, now I think of it, I have a bottle of excellent nectar which Pallas gave me; if you have a mind, I will give you a dram to whet your whistle."

The Grasshopper, ready to die with thirst, and at the same time pleased to be so complimented upon account of her playing, skipped up to the place very briskly; when the Owl, advancing to meet her, seized, and without much delay made her a sacrifice to her revenge, securing to herself by the death of her enemy, a possession of that quiet which during her lifetime she could not enjoy.

WHEN THE ENEMY FLATTERS, BE ON YOUR GUARD.

THE HAWK AND THE FARMER

A Hawk, pursuing a pigeon over a cornfield with great eagerness and force, threw herself into a net which a husbandman had planted there to take the crows, who, being employed not far off, and seeing the Hawk fluttering in the net, came and took him; but just as he was going to kill him the Hawk besought him to let him go, assuring him that he was only following a Pigeon, and neither intended nor had done any harm to him.   To whom the Farmer replied :

" And what harm had the poor Pigeon done to you ?"

Upon which he wrung his head off immediately.

THE OPPRESSOR CANNOT HOPE FOR MERCY.

THE PARTRIDGE
AND THE COCKS

A CERTAIN man, having taken a Partridge, plucked some of the feathers out of its wings, and turned it into a little yard where he kept gamecocks. The Cocks for a while made the poor bird lead a sad life, continually pecking and driving it away from the meat. This treatment was taken the more unkindly because offered to a stranger; and the Partridge could not but consider them the most inhospitable and uncivil people he had ever met. But at last, observing how frequently they quarrelled and fought with each other, he comforted himself with this reflection, that it was no wonder they were so cruel to him, since there was so much bickering and animosity among themselves.

THE FROGS AND THE FIGHTING BULLS

A Frog one day, peeping out of the lake and looking about him, saw two Bulls fighting at some distance off in the meadow; and, calling to one of his acquaintance:

"Look," says he, "what dreadful work is yonder. Dear sir, what will become of us?"

"Why, pray thee," says the other, "do not frighten yourself so about nothing. How can their quarrels affect us? They are of a different kind and way of living, and are at present only contending which shall be master of the herd."

"That is true," replies the first; "their quality and station in life is, to all appearance, different enough from ours. But as one of them will certainly get the better, he that is worsted being beat out of the meadow, will take refuge here in the marshes, and may possibly tread upon some of us; so you see, we are more nearly concerned in this dispute of theirs than at first you were aware of."

THE CONFLICTS OF THE GREAT CONCERN THE HUMBLE.

A MAN BITTEN BY A DOG

A MAN who had been sadly torn by a Dog was advised by some old women, as a cure, to dip a piece of bread in the wound and give it to the cur that bit him. He did so; and Æsop, happening to pass by just at the same time, asked him what he meant by it. The Man informed him.

"Why, then," says Æsop, "do it as privately as you can I beseech you, for if the rest of the Dogs of the town were to see you, we should all be eaten up alive by them."

A SUCCESSFUL ROGUE LEADS OTHERS TO IMITATE HIS MISDEEDS.

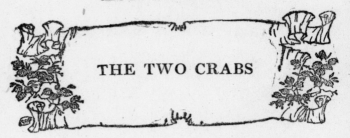

THE TWO CRABS

IT is said to be the nature of a Crab fish to walk backwards. However, a Mother-Crab one day reproved her daughter, and was in a great passion with her for her awkward gait, which she desired her to alter, and not to move in a way so contradictory to the rest of the world.

"Indeed, Mother," says the young Crab, "I walk as decently as I can and to the best of my knowledge; but if you would have me go otherwise I beg you would be so good as to practise it first, and show me, by your own example, how you would have me behave myself."

PRACTISE WHAT YOU PREACH.

THE TWO FROGS

ONE hot, sultry summer, the lakes and ponds being almost everywhere dried up, a couple of Frogs agreed to travel together in search of water. At last they came to a deep well, and, sitting upon the brink of it, began to consult whether they should leap in or not. One of them was for it, urging that there was plenty of clear spring water, and no danger of being disturbed.

"Well," says the other, "all this may be true; and yet I cannot come to your opinion for my life, for if the water should happen to dry up here too, how should we get out again?"

LOOK BEFORE YOU LEAP.

THE OLD WOMAN AND THE EMPTY CASK

An Old Woman saw an empty Cask, from which there had been lately drawn some choice, racy palm-sack, the spirit of which yet hung about the barrel, and the very lees yielded a grateful cordial scent. She applied her nose to the bung-hole, and snuffing very heartily for some time, at last broke out into this exclamation:

"Oh, the delicious smell! How good, how good you must have been once when your very dregs are so agreeable and refreshing."

THE MISCHIEVOUS DOG

A CERTAIN man had a Dog which was so mischievous that he was forced to fasten a heavy clog about his neck, to keep him from running at and worrying people. This the vain cur took for a badge of honourable distinction; and grew so insolent upon it that he looked down with an air of scorn upon the neighbouring Dogs, and refused to keep them company. But a sly old poacher, who was one of the gang, assured him that he had no reason to value himself upon the favour he wore, since it was fixed upon him rather as a mark of disgrace than of honour.

NOTORIETY IS NOT HONOUR.

THE FOX AND
THE GOAT

A Fox, having tumbled by chance into a well, had been casting about a long while, to no purpose, how he should get out again; when at last a Goat came to the place, and, wanting to drink, asked Reynard whether the water was good.

"Good!" says he. "Ay, so sweet that I am afraid I have had too much. I have drunk so abundantly."

The Goat upon this, without any more ado, leapt in; and the Fox, taking the advantage of his horns, by the assistance of them as nimbly leapt out, leaving the poor Goat at the bottom of the well to shift for himself.

IT IS FOOLISH TO TAKE THE ADVICE OF THOSE WHO ARE IN
DIFFICULTIES.